D0323854

Ciba Foundation
Study Group No. 36

HORMONES AND THE
IMMUNE RESPONSE

HORMONES AND THE IMMUNE RESPONSE

Ciba Foundation
Study Group No. 36

Edited by
G. E. W. WOLSTENHOLME
and
JULIE KNIGHT

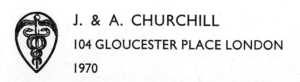

J. & A. CHURCHILL
104 GLOUCESTER PLACE LONDON
1970

First published 1970

With 35 illustrations

I.S.B.N. 0.7000. 1464.0

Printed in Great Britain

Contents

Membership

Study Group on Hormones and the Immune Response, held 1st May 1970

J. H. Humphrey (Chairman)	National Institute for Medical Research, Mill Hill, London N.W.7, England
C. T. Ambrose	Department of Bacteriology and Immunology, Harvard Medical School, 25 Shattuck Street, Boston, Massachusetts 02115, U.S.A.
H. Bloch	CIBA Limited, 4000 Basel, Switzerland
U. Ernström	Department of Histology, Karolinska Institutet, Solnavägen 1, Stockholm 60, Sweden
N. Fabris	Medizinische Abteilung, Schweizerisches Forschungsinstitut, 7270 Davos-Platz, Switzerland
J. Fachet	Department of Pathophysiology, Research Institute of Experimental Medicine, Hungarian Academy of Science, Budapest, Hungary
A. L. Goldstein	Department of Biochemistry, Albert Einstein College of Medicine, Yeshiva University, 1300 Morris Park Avenue, Bronx, N.Y. 10461, U.S.A.
A. Gunn	Department of Surgery, The University, Dundee, Scotland
D. N. Hamilton	National Institute for Medical Research, Mill Hill, London N.W.7, England
R. J. B. King	Hormone Biochemistry Department, Imperial Cancer Research Fund, Lincoln's Inn Fields, London W.C.2, England
A. Korner	Department of Biochemistry, University of Sussex, Falmer, Brighton BN1 9QG, England
E. M. Lance	Hospital for Special Surgery, 535 East 70 St, New York, N.Y. 10021, U.S.A.
W. I. P. Mainwaring	Division of Chemistry and Biochemistry, Imperial Cancer Research Fund, Lincoln's Inn Fields, London W.C.2, England
O. Mühlbock	The Netherlands Cancer Institute, Antoni van Leeuwenhoek-Huis, Sarphatistraat 108, Amsterdam C, The Netherlands

The Ciba Foundation

The Ciba Foundation was opened in 1949 to promote international cooperation in medical and chemical research. It owes its existence to the generosity of CIBA Ltd, Basle, who, recognizing the obstacles to scientific communication created by war, man's natural secretiveness, disciplinary divisions, academic prejudices, distance, and differences of language, decided to set up a philanthropic institution whose aim would be to overcome such barriers. London was chosen as its site for reasons dictated by the special advantages of English charitable trust law (ensuring the independence of its actions), as well as those of language and geography.

The Foundation's house at 41 Portland Place, London, has become well known to workers in many fields of science. Every year the Foundation organizes six to ten three-day symposia and three or four shorter study groups, all of which are published in book form. Many other scientific meetings are held, organized either by the Foundation or by other groups in need of a meeting place. Accommodation is also provided for scientists visiting London, whether or not they are attending a meeting in the house.

The Foundation's many activities are controlled by a small group of distinguished trustees. Within the general framework of biological science, interpreted in its broadest sense, these activities are well summed up by the motto of the Ciba Foundation: *Consocient Gentes*—let the peoples come together.

CHAIRMAN'S OPENING REMARKS

Dr J. H. Humphrey

I AM acting as Chairman on behalf of Sir Peter Medawar whose interest in the effects of hormones on the immune response has existed almost as long as his interest in the response itself, beginning with his studies on cortisone at a time when our ignorance was much greater than it is now (Billingham, Krohn and Medawar 1951a, b; Medawar and Sparrow 1956). One reason for asking Dr Wolstenholme to hold this meeting was that Sir Peter and his colleagues have some very promising findings of synergism between cortisone and antilymphocytic serum (ALS) which you will hear about during this meeting. Equally or more important is the fact that clear-cut evidence of effects not only of corticosteroids but of other hormones has been produced in recent years, and in the light of new knowledge of the cellular basis of the immune response they begin to be interpretable. The Ciba Foundation provides a good environment for persons who have approached the problem of the effects of hormones on the immune response from a variety of different angles to pool their experience.

Before this meeting I looked up Thomas Dougherty's 1952 review on the effect of hormones on lymphatic tissue, and I was interested to see that with the wisdom of hindsight one could have picked out from it a number of the topics which will be brought up today. Evidence for example, that growth hormone increases thymus weight; that adrenalectomy increases the weight of lymphoid tissues throughout the body; that glucocorticoids decrease it, as do oestrogens and androgens; that thyroid hormone increases the weight of lymphoid tissue and the size of the immune response. But for nearly all the positive evidence cited in Dougherty's review he cited evidence to the contrary, and the fact is that 20 years ago the situation was difficult to untangle. This was partly because at the time when he surveyed the literature each powerful hormone as it was isolated had almost automatically been tested on the "immune response", among other things, but what was called the immune response might be the response of a rabbit or a rat to a large dose of soluble antigen, or the response of a guinea pig to a small dose of something else, and so on, and the amounts of hormone administered were seldom physiological, and often enormous. So it is not surprising that it was impossible, even for a person of great ability, to produce any very clear statements about how hormones govern the immune response.

We now know a great deal more about what is going on. We can draw a clear distinction between cell-mediated immunity on the one hand, and antibody-mediated immunity on the other, and we are aware that several classes of antibody are produced; we know that there may be big differences between responses to small quantities of antigen administered in some form of adjuvant and to large amounts administered in soluble form. We recognize that many situations represent a balance between concomitant immunization and tolerance. We know that the effect of an antigen depends not only on the response of the lymphocyte to it, but also upon the fate of the antigen in tissues, what cell it has been taken up by, and what is the micro-environment in which interaction between it and the specifically responsive lymphocytes takes place. Lastly, we are aware that lymphocytes comprise at least two distinct populations, one thymus derived and the other not. The latter, called rather indeterminately bone marrow derived in mammals but known to be bursa dependent in birds, appear on present evidence to be solely responsible for antibody production, but this function is rendered much more efficient by specific cooperation with thymus derived lymphocytes. If hormones have differential effects on the two populations the consequences for the immune response are likely to be complicated. In fact it appears, as our speakers will tell us, that some well defined hormones and other less well characterized substances do have marked and often differential effects on the development and capacities of lymphocytes. Our discussion may not end with us knowing all the answers, but it will certainly help to clarify the questions.

REFERENCES

BILLINGHAM, R. E., KROHN, P. L. and MEDAWAR, P. B. (1951a) Br. med. J. **1,** 1157–1163.

BILLINGHAM, R. E., KROHN, P. L. and MEDAWAR, P. B. (1951b) Br. med. J. **2,** 1049–1053.

DOUGHERTY, T. F. (1952) Physiol. Rev. **32,** 379.

MEDAWAR, P. B. and SPARROW, E. M. (1956) J. Endocr. **14,** 240.

THYMOSIN, A THYMIC HORMONE INFLUENCING LYMPHOID CELL IMMUNOLOGICAL COMPETENCE

ABRAHAM WHITE AND ALLAN L. GOLDSTEIN

Department of Biochemistry, Albert Einstein College of Medicine, Yeshiva University, Bronx, New York

STUDIES of the thymus gland over the past decade have established a central role in a number of animal species, including the human, for the thymus gland in the development and expression of lymphoid tissue structure and function. It is now well documented that the full expression of host immunity, particularly cell-mediated phenomena, depends for the most part on a normally functioning thymus gland (cf. Good and Gabrielson 1964; Good 1967; Miller 1967; Miller and Osoba 1967; Hess 1968; Alexander and Good 1970; Gatti, Stutman and Good 1970; Goldstein *et al.* 1970*a*; Goldstein, Asanuma and White 1970; Goldstein and White 1970*a, b*; White and Goldstein 1970*a, b*).

Congenital absence or dysfunction of the thymus gland in the human, as, for example, in infants with the DiGeorge syndrome (DiGeorge 1968), is characterized by almost total absence of cell-mediated responses, an extreme lymphopenia and a marked susceptibility to a wide variety of infectious agents, particularly those of a viral or fungal nature. This syndrome is incompatible with life and infants with this affliction usually succumb before six months of age. Similarly, congenital aplasia of the thymus gland in mice (Rygaard 1969) or experimental neonatal thymectomy (Archer and Pierce 1961; Miller 1961; Good *et al.* 1962) results in a severe lymphopenia, almost total failure of development of cell-mediated immunological capacities and extreme susceptibility to infectious agents. Most species of mice develop a "wasting" disease which is characterized by widespread infection which usually culminates in death of the experimental animal.

In contrast to the major crippling effects on cell-mediated immunity of neonatal thymectomy in animals or of congenital thymic aplasia in the human, there is evident only a minor influence on humoral antibody production. Neonatally thymectomized mice, for example, can produce normal antibody titres to such antigens as ferritin (Fahey, Barth and Law 1965), polyoma virus (Miller, Ting and Law 1964), or haemocyanin (Humphrey, Parrott and East 1964) but exhibit a reduced capacity to synthesize antibody after a primary challenge to other antigens such as sheep erythrocytes (Osoba and Miller 1964). In man, thymic aplasia is similarly not associated with marked defects in humoral capacity (DiGeorge 1968). Thus, the primary influence of the thymus appears to be on the more primitive lymphoid cells that will eventually mature into classes of lymphoid cells endowed with the capacity to function as immunologically competent lymphoid cells in cell-mediated immune responses.

The mechanism by which the thymus endows lymphoid stem cells with immunological competence is not understood. Evidence has been provided to support both an endocrine and a cellular mechanism. The endocrine hypothesis suggests that lymphoid stem cells from the bone marrow, spleen and other peripheral tissues mature under the influence of thymosin or other thymic hormones to become part of the pool of immunologically competent cells which can then respond to antigenic stimuli. The evidence that thymosin and other possible thymic hormones can act peripherally in lieu of the thymus derives from experiments in which neonatally thymectomized mice were reconstituted with cell-free thymic extracts (Asanuma, Goldstein and White 1970; Trainin et al. 1966; Trainin, Burger and Kaye 1967; Law, Goldstein and White 1968; Goldstein et al. 1970a; White and Goldstein 1970a) and with thymic grafts (cf. Miller and Osoba 1967) or with reticuloepithelial thymomas placed in cell-impermeable Millipore chambers (Stutman, Yunis and Good 1969).

The cellular hypothesis of thymic function proposes that lymphoid stem cells which either have migrated into the thymus gland from peripheral sites or are indigenous to the thymus require a thymic locus in order to achieve maturity. In an animal with a thymus, thymosin or other thymic factors may not be released from the gland but might act *in situ* on these cell populations to induce maturity. Once mature, these thymus-housed and nurtured cells are then seeded to the periphery where they enter the pool of immunologically competent cells. Chromosomal marker (Ford and Micklem 1963) and isotopic labelling studies (cf. Gowans 1969; Gowans and McGregor 1965) of cell populations have demonstrated this pattern of redistribution of cells. In addition, thymocytes, although not as effective as equal numbers of mature lymphocytes, have the capacity to reconstitute neonatally thymectomized mice (Miller and Mitchell 1968) and have also been shown to have the capacity to elicit graft-versus-host reactions (Cohen *et al.* 1963) as well as to participate as the antigen-recognition cells in the humoral antibody response to sheep erythrocytes (Mitchell and Miller 1968).

In 1966, we reported the extraction and partial purification of a cell-free preparation from calf thymus which we termed thymosin (Goldstein, Slater and White 1966). Thymosin produced a proliferation of lymphoid tissue when administered to normal adult mice. The end-point of the proliferative effect was reflected in an increase in the absolute size of the lymphoid tissue and in a stimulation of incorporation of precursors into macromolecular components of lymphoid cells, such as DNA, RNA and protein.

Subsequently, we have demonstrated that thymosin is also lymphocytopoietic in either neonatally thymectomized, sublethally or lethally irradiated mice and in normal guinea pigs. Here we shall outline briefly the further purification of this material (cf. also Goldstein, Asanuma and White 1970) and then describe experiments designed to assess the effects of thymosin on humoral antibody production and on cell-mediated immune phenomena.

PREPARATION OF THYMOSIN

The lymphocytopoietic factor which we have termed thymosin was initially isolated from mouse thymus. At a later time we used rat thymic tissue and, finally, for greater quantities of material, we have turned to calf thymus as the source tissue. Thymosin activity is present in the thymus of all species that we have examined, including the human. At the present stage of purification we have achieved approximately a 200-fold purification of thymosin. The biological activity of our preparation is either identical with or very closely associated with a protein; the best estimate of its molecular weight at the moment is less than 100 000, although this is difficult to establish precisely since the protein has a tendency to aggregate. The most highly purified thymosin preparation does not contain nucleic acid; it is not inactivated by incubation with RNase or DNase, but is inactivated by incubation with proteolytic enzymes. The most purified thymosin preparation contains less than 1 per cent of carbohydrate and a trace of lipid; this lipid, however, is not essential for its biological activity. This purified fraction reveals one major and two minor components on polyacrylamide gel electrophoresis, all migrating toward the anode at pH 8·3.

BIOLOGICAL STUDIES WITH THYMOSIN

Activity of thymosin in neonatally thymectomized mice

Thymosin is biologically active in neonatally thymectomized mice. In all of these experiments we use our own line of CBA mice, bred in our laboratory and designated as CBA/Wh. Table I contains data assembled from several studies designed to examine whether thymosin treatment of neonatally thymectomized mice would influence their survival and two parameters reflecting host immunological competence, namely, humoral (19S) antibody synthesis and cell-mediated immunity.

The following conclusions may be drawn from the data in Table I. The administration of thymosin to neonatally thymectomized mice increased significantly the ability of these operated animals to survive. Partial restoration of lymphoid cell populations to lymph nodes and peripheral blood was also seen in the thymosin-treated group of neonatally thymectomized mice (Asanuma, Goldstein and White 1970).

From Table I, the lack of influence of the other fractions tested, including endotoxin, on survival of the neonatally thymectomized mice is evident. The absence of any beneficial effect of endotoxin, which non-specifically stimulates proliferation of lymphoid tissue in the neonatally thymectomized animal, is in agreement with the earlier study of Salvin, Peterson and Good (1965). They found that neonatally thymectomized mice are three to ten times more susceptible to the lethal effects of endotoxin than are normal mice.

The second conclusion from the data in Table I is that giving thymosin to neonatally thymectomized mice had little influence on their ability to respond immunologically to a challenge of

TABLE I

INFLUENCE OF THYMOSIN ADMINISTRATION TO NEONATALLY THYMECTO-
MIZED CBA/WH MICE ON HOST IMMUNOLOGICAL RESPONSES

Group*	Percentage survival at 63 days	Average number of plaque-forming cells per spleen** (range of values)	Allograft survival†
Normal, unoperated	100	26 509 (7800–88 000)	0/14
Thymectomy + 0·15 M–NaCl	33	845 (150–2400)	12/16
Thymectomy + bovine serum albumin‡	30	892 (500–1500)	2/4
Thymectomy + calf spleen fraction‡	25	—	4/4
Thymectomy + endo- toxin§	30	—	11/13
Thymectomy + thy- mosin‡	70	3399 (200–13 450)	1/22

The data in this table are assembled in part from Asanuma, Goldstein and White (1970) and Goldstein and co-workers (1970a), as well as from unpublished results.

*The number of animals initially in each group varied from 14 in the normal, unoperated group to 40 in the thymosin-treated group. Thymectomy, where performed, was within 24 hours of birth.

**Animals in each group treated, as indicated, for 63 days postnatally. At 91 days of age, surviving mice received 1·0 ml of a 2·5 per cent suspension of sheep erythrocytes intraperitoneally. Animals were sacrificed four days later and their spleens examined for direct plaque-forming cells by the technique of Jerne and Nordin (1963).

†A/J skin allograft placed on mice at 63 days of age. The data in this column are the number of allografts surviving at 32 days after grafting, given as the number of intact A/J skin grafts/total number of mice per group.

‡Each animal received 0·5 mg protein, in 0·2 ml 0·15 M-NaCl, intraperitoneally 3 times during the first week and 1·0 mg protein, in 0·2 ml 0·15 M-NaCl, sub-cutaneously 3 times during each of the second to ninth weeks.

§Salmonella enteritidis, 10 µg per injection, 3 times a week for 9 weeks.

sheep erythrocytes. In our experience, we have found a rather wide range of values for plaque-forming cells in the spleens of either normal or thymectomized mice injected with sheep erythrocytes. The numbers of these cells in thymectomized animals were characteristically depressed, as has been often described. The thymosin-treated animals, while having slightly higher levels of plaque-forming cells in their spleens than did the control, saline-treated thymectomized mice, were not significantly different statistically.

In contrast to the failure of thymosin to influence 19S antibody formation, the data in Table I reveal that the normal unoperated control animals all rejected skin allografts in less than 12 days because of the presence of their thymuses. Similarly, 21 of 22 neonatally thymectomized animals treated with thymosin had a restored capacity to reject an allograft, with graft rejection occurring in less than 16 days. In marked contrast, most of the animals treated with saline, bovine serum albumin, a calf spleen fraction, or *Salmonella enteritidis* endotoxin had intact allografts 32 days after grafting. Thus the data indicate that at a time at which thymosin has little influence on the ability of the neonatally thymectomized mouse to synthesize 19S antibody to sheep erythrocytes, it has restored to the operated animals the capacity to reject a skin allograft, a phenomenon which reflects the degree of host cell-mediated immunity. It may be concluded that the effectiveness of thymosin administration in prolonging the survival of neonatally thymectomized mice and in restoring their capacity to reject a skin allograft is a specific property of thymosin and is not mimicked by other calf tissue fractions such as spleen, or by other antigens which may non-specifically proliferate lymphoid tissue, such as bovine serum albumin or endotoxins.

It may be noted that in other experiments (Goldstein *et al.* 1970*a*) we have also been unable to demonstrate an influence of thymosin on 19S antibody formation in either normal mice or adult, thymectomized, lethally irradiated (800R) mice maintained with bone marrow and challenged with sheep erythrocytes.

In collaboration with Dr Lloyd Law of the National Cancer Institute we have reported previously that giving thymosin to neonatally thymectomized C57BL/KaLw mice restored to their spleen cells the ability to elicit a graft-versus-host (GVH) reaction when injected into BALB/c mice (Law, Goldstein and White 1968). In contrast, a preparation made in precisely the same way from calf spleen as the thymosin from calf thymus did not restore to the spleen cells of these neonatally thymectomized animals their capacity to elicit a GVH reaction. Thus, in this experimental design, as in the allograft study, giving thymosin to the neonatally thymectomized animal restored the capacity of cells of the treated animal to participate in a cell-mediated immune phenomenon. The use of the GVH reaction has now been extended in the studies described below.

Effect of thymosin on the rate of maturation of immature lymphoid cells to immunologically competent cells

We have explored the question of whether the maturation of lymphoid stem cells into immunologically competent cells can be accelerated by the exposure of these cells to thymosin either *in vivo* or *in vitro*, utilizing the graft-versus-host response in adult, lethally irradiated histoincompatible mice. Spleen or bone marrow cells (5×10^6) from CBA/Wh mice have been administered intraperitoneally or intravenously to adult, lethally irradiated (800 R) B6AF1/J mice. The recipient mice are sacrificed 7 days later and the ratio of the spleen weight (in milligrammes) to body weight (in grammes) is determined. The comparison of this ratio in a group of experimental mice to that obtained from a group of control mice given similar numbers of syngeneic cells yields a second ratio, termed the spleen index. A spleen index of greater than 1·3 is usually considered a significant GVH reaction (Simonsen 1962).

The data in Table II indicate that when thymosin, in three differing dosages, is administered on days 1 and 2 of life to newborn CBA/Wh mice, the spleen cells of these animals show a capacity to elicit the GVH reaction when taken from mice only 4 days of age, at a time when this immunological development in untreated mice of the same age (saline group) is just being initiated.

TABLE II

ACCELERATED DEVELOPMENT BY THYMOSIN *IN VIVO* OF IMMUNOLOGICAL COMPETENCE

Experimental groups*	Number of host animals**	Spleen wt.(mg) / Body wt.(g)	p values	Spleen index
Saline	22	2·15±0·14†		1·31
25 μg thymosin	26	2·95±0·16	<0·01	1·80
2·5 μg thymosin	14	3·19±0·18	<0·01	1·95
0·25 μg thymosin	9	3·38±0·28	<0·01	2·06
2·5 μg calf spleen fraction 8	7	2·59±0·22	>0·1	1·58

*CBA/Wh mice.

**Each B6AF1/J host was exposed to 800 R whole body X-irradiation, and then injected intravenously with 5×10^6 nucleated spleen cells from groups of 4-day-old CBA/Wh mice treated as indicated on days 1 and 2.

†Mean values ± standard errors.

(After Goldstein *et al.* 1970b, submitted for publication.)

Moreover, a calf spleen fraction, prepared in the same manner as thymosin, is inactive in this assay system.

The maturation of immunological competence of spleen cells *in vitro* has also been accelerated by incubating spleen cells from three-day-old CBA/Wh mice with 1 mg or 0·1 mg of thymosin per 10^7 cells (Table III). After incubation for $1\frac{1}{2}$ hours, $5·0 \times 10^6$

TABLE III

ACCELERATED DEVELOPMENT BY THYMOSIN *IN VITRO* OF IMMUNOLOGICAL COMPETENCE

Experimental groups	Number of host animals[*]	Spleen wt.(mg) / Body wt.(g)	p values	Spleen index
Saline	36	1·23 ± 0·03[†]		1·11
1 mg thymosin[**]	25	1·45 ± 0·6	<0·01	1·31
0·1 mg thymosin	8	1·69 ± 0·19	<0·01	1·52
0·04 mg thymosin	5	1·40 ± 0·13	>0·1	1·26
0·1 mg spleen fraction	14	1·17 ± 0·03	>0·3	1·05

[*]Each B6AF1/J host was exposed to 800 R whole body X-irradiation, and then injected within 2 hours intraperitoneally with 5×10^6 nucleated spleen cells from 3-day-old CBA/Wh mice incubated *in vitro* as indicated in the several experimental groups.

[**]Each concentration per 1×10^7 cells in medium RPMI-1640 with 10 per cent foetal calf serum for $1·5$ hours at 37 °C, with air–10 per cent CO_2 as gas phase.

[†]Mean values ± standard errors.

(After Goldstein *et al.* 1970b, submitted for publication.)

of these cells were injected into the lethally irradiated B6AF1/J host. The mice were sacrificed 7 days later, as above. The data reveal that with either dose of thymosin, spleen cells taken from three-day-old mice which are normally not immunologically competent in this assay, now exhibit immunological competence as measured by the GVH reaction. Spleen cells incubated with a calf spleen fraction prepared in the same way as thymosin did not induce a GVH reaction.

Similar studies have also been made with bone marrow cells incubated *in vitro* with thymosin. Some of the results obtained are presented in Table IV. The data reveal that relatively small quantities of thymosin added *in vitro* to immunologically incompetent bone marrow cells stimulate the latent capacity of these cells to elicit a GVH reaction *in vivo*. The data also suggest that bone marrow cells are somewhat more responsive to thymosin

TABLE IV

STIMULATION BY THYMOSIN *IN VITRO* OF GRAFT–VERSUS–HOST REACTIVITY OF ALLOGENEIC BONE MARROW CELLS

Experimental groups*	Number of host animals**	$\dfrac{Spleen\ wt.(mg)}{Body\ wt.(g)}$	p values	Spleen index
B6AF1/J bone marrow cells (syngeneic)	60	$2 \cdot 08 \pm 0 \cdot 10$†		
CBA/Wh bone marrow cells (allogeneic):				
+ Saline	62	$2 \cdot 65 \pm 0 \cdot 10$		$1 \cdot 27$
+ 100 μg thymosin, fraction 3	28	$3 \cdot 74 \pm 0 \cdot 36$	$< 0 \cdot 01$	$1 \cdot 80$
+ 10 μg thymosin, fraction 3	21	$3 \cdot 99 \pm 0 \cdot 30$	$< 0 \cdot 01$	$1 \cdot 92$
+ 1 μg thymosin, fraction 3	9	$3 \cdot 78 \pm 0 \cdot 37$	$< 0 \cdot 01$	$1 \cdot 82$
+ 100 μg spleen, fraction 3	8	$3 \cdot 23 \pm 0 \cdot 40$	$> 0 \cdot 05$	$1 \cdot 55$
+ 10 μg spleen, fraction 3	12	$2 \cdot 97 \pm 0 \cdot 17$	$> 0 \cdot 2$	$1 \cdot 43$
+ 1 μg spleen, fraction 3	8	$2 \cdot 45 \pm 0 \cdot 23$	$> 0 \cdot 5$	$1 \cdot 18$

*Each concentration per 1×10^7 cells incubated *in vitro* in medium RPMI-1640 with 10 per cent foetal calf serum for $1 \cdot 5$ hours at 37 °C, with air–10 per cent CO_2 as gas phase.

**Each B6AF1/J host was exposed to 800 R whole body X-irradiation and then injected intravenously within 2 hours with 5×10^6 nucleated bone marrow cells previously incubated *in vitro* as indicated in the several experimental groups.

†Mean± standard errors.

(After Goldstein *et al.* 1970*b*, submitted for publication.)

than are spleen cells of the same mouse strain under the experimental conditions used.

Effect of thymosin on cell-mediated resistance to a virus-induced tumour in mice

We have investigated the influence of thymosin in another system which also reflects host-cell mediated immunity. Injection of the Moloney sarcoma virus into the thigh muscle of a CBA/Wh mouse results in the development of a tumour generally within

4–6 days following inoculation. Depending upon the dose of virus used, in a normal, immunologically competent animal the tumour regresses within a period of 20–30 days. It has been established that this regression is primarily a cell-mediated immune phenomenon. In adult CBA/Wh mice, with the dose of virus used (0·1 ml of 1:10 dilution, Lot number 144-R, provided by Dr G. B. Moloney of the National Cancer Institute) 100 per cent of the animals developed a sarcoma and all mice survived. In contrast, newborn mice had no immunological competence for suppressing the growth of the tumour and at 60 days none of the animals injected with virus at birth had survived, nor had those injected at one week of age. Fig. 1 indicates that immunological

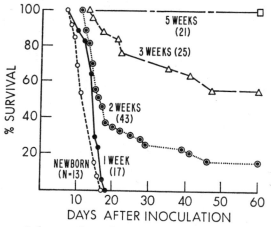

Fig. 1. Influence of age of CBA/Wh mice on their resistance to progressive tumour growth. Age at time of inoculation as indicated; number of animals in each group in parentheses. (From Zisblatt *et al.* 1970.)

competence with respect to the suppression of the progressive growth of this virus-induced tumour begins to develop in CBA/Wh mice between the first and second weeks of life; is isgnificant by 3 weeks of age, and at 5 weeks of age the mice are completely capable of suppressing further growth of the tumour, although all 5-week-old animals injected with virus develop the tumour within 4–6 days following inoculation. However, if mice are thymectomized at birth and then challenged with virus at 5 weeks of age, they are unable to suppress the further growth of the tumour and death results (unpublished results).

Figure 2 presents data obtained in an experiment in which mice were injected with 0·5 mg thymosin protein three times a week during the first week of life, 1·0 mg three times a week during the second week, and then challenged with the Moloney virus. The rate of survival at 60 days of age of these thymosin-treated

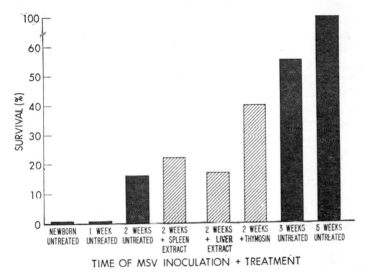

FIG. 2. Development of resistance to progressive tumour growth in CBA/Wh mice inoculated with murine sarcoma virus (Moloney) (MSV) at the time indicated. The groups consist of untreated controls or of mice treated with either thymosin or a calf spleen or calf liver fraction prior to viral inoculation. Schedule of treatment is in the text. The data depicted are representative of 13 to 43 mice in each group and indicate the percentage that had survived 60 days after inoculation with the virus. (From Zisblatt *et al.* 1970.)

mice was approximately double that of mice which had been injected with similar quantities of protein in the form of either a calf spleen or liver fraction and then challenged with the virus. Statistical analysis of the data indicates that a two-week-old

mouse treated from birth with thymosin has acquired the immunological competence of a three-week-old untreated animal with
respect to its capacity to resist progressive growth of the tumour.
That is, thymosin accelerated the normal development of resistance to progressive tumour growth following inoculation with
this oncogenic virus.

In conclusion, we wish to present a hypothesis which has
evolved from the newly defined roles of the thymus as an endocrine gland. This hypothesis is based upon the experimental
evidence that thymosin, probably secreted by the reticuloepithelial
cells of the thymus, can act in lieu of the thymus to restore cell-
mediated immunological competence in a number of experimental systems but is without action on humoral antibody
synthesis (Goldstein *et al.* 1970*a*; Goldstein and White 1970*a*, *b*;
White and Goldstein 1970*a*, *b*). These findings suggest that there
are at least two populations of thymus-dependent immunologically competent cells, in addition to at least one large class of
thymus-independent cells, namely, potential antibody-producing
cells. The latter class includes the cells that act in cooperation with
a thymus-dependent cell in the production of humoral antibody
(Clamen, Chaperon and Triplett 1966; Mitchell and Miller 1968).

Figure 3 shows our present concept of the maturation of the two
classes of thymus-dependent immunologically competent cells.
One type, termed Class *A* cells, can mature under the influence
solely of thymosin acting upon stem cell precursors (pre- or post-
thymic cell populations) from bone marrow, spleen, liver,
Peyer's patches or other peripheral sites and not requiring an
in situ thymic locus. The experimental findings presented here and
elsewhere (Goldstein *et al.* 1970*b*) suggest that the maturation of
this type of immunologically competent cell occurs rapidly and
might involve derepression or activation of an incompetent cell
at a specific stage in its differentiation. The development of Class
A cells could occur either within or outside the thymic environment. The second type of lymphocyte, which we have termed
Class *B* cells, consists of the thymus-dependent cells involved in
humoral immunity. This type of cell, once mature, can recognize
either soluble antigens or antigens which have been solubilized by
macrophages, and is capable of acting in cooperation with a
population of thymus-independent cells (Class *C* cells) which
contain the antibody-producing mechanism and thus are necessary

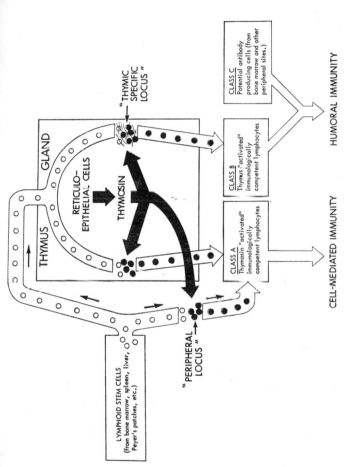

FIG. 3. Schematic representation of the role of thymosin in the development of immunologically competent cells. See text for details.

to elicit a humoral response. Our experimental findings indicate that the maturation of Class *B* lymphocytes requires specifically, in contrast to Class *A* lymphocytes, an intact thymic locus for proper development, as well as thymosin and/or other thymic factors. Thus, the stem cell from which Class *B* cells arise must, at some time in its development, reside within the thymus proper. The distinction between the two classes of thymus-dependent cells appears to be based upon whether or not maturation must occur within the thymic environment.

Numerous studies in the literature indicate that cells involved in cell-mediated responses are present within the thymus. It thus appears that in a normal animal the development of Class *A* cells can occur within the thymic environment, as well as peripherally. Our recent studies of the reconstitution of neonatally thymectomized mice by administration of thymosin (Law, Goldstein and White 1968; Asanuma, Goldstein and White 1970; Goldstein *et al.* 1970*a*) indicate that a thymic locus is not, however, an absolute requirement for the maturation of these cells. It is possible that the extremely high mitotic index within the thymus is a reflection of the influence of thymic humoral factors on the maturation and/or expansion of both Class *A* and Class *B* cells that are either indigenous to the thymus or have entered the gland from the periphery.

The availability of new methods to separate distinct populations of viable lymphoid cells and the isolation and purification of thymosin offer the possibility of dissecting the intricate processes by which lymphoid cells mature, and perhaps of clarifying the contribution of the thymus gland to the normal functioning of cells of the lymphoid system.

SUMMARY

A brief description is given of the chemical properties of a fraction obtained from calf thymic tissue which was initially characterized by its lymphocytopoietic activity and has been termed thymosin. Thymosin activity is either identical to, or closely associated with, a protein. Thymosin is lymphocyto-poietic in normal, adrenalectomized, neonatally thymectomized, sublethally and lethally X-irradiated mice. Thymosin given to neonatally thymectomized mice reduces the incidence of wasting disease and maintains partially the normal histological appearance of their lymphoid tissue, notably the thymus-dependent areas of the lymph nodes and spleen. In the neonatally thymectomized mice, thymosin injection leads to normal development of cell-mediated immunological competence as reflected in the ability to reject a skin allograft. In addition, thymosin given to neonatal mice, or thymosin incubated with immunologically incompetent spleen or bone marrow cells *in vitro*, accelerates the rate of maturation of immunological competence of lymphoid cells as reflected in a graft-versus-host assay. In contrast, thymosin given to neonatally thymectomized mice, or to normal adult mice, or to adult, thymectomized, lethally X-irradiated mice maintained with bone marrow, does not influence their capacity to synthesize humoral antibody in response to a challenging dose of sheep erythrocytes. Control animals receiving either saline, bovine serum albumin, calf spleen or liver fractions, or endotoxin showed no restoration of any of the thymus-dependent, cell mediated immunological phenomena which were improved by injection of thymosin.

At present, it is concluded that thymosin may influence the rate of maturation of immunological competence in more primitive, potentially competent lymphoid cells. The latter may, or may not, require the intact thymus gland to express the influence of thymosin on the maturation of immunological competence. This conclusion has led us to postulate at least three broad classes of small lymphocytes, *one* which can mature solely under the influence of thymosin and functions primarily in cell-mediated immune phenomena, a *second* which requires a thymic locus for development and is involved primarily in humoral immune phenomena, in cooperation with a *third* class of thymus-independent lymphoid cells.

Acknowledgements

The studies described in this paper have been made possible by the generous collaboration of the following colleagues at the Albert Einstein College of Medicine: Dr J. R. Battisto of the Department of Microbiology and Immunology, Dr M. A. Hardy and Dr J. Quint of the Department of Surgery, and Dr F. Lilly and Dr M. Zisblatt of the Department of Genetics. Valuable technical assistance was provided by Mrs Roshalee Levine, Miss Norma Robert and Mr James Oliver.

The data in this paper from the authors' laboratory derive from investigations supported by grants from the National Cancer Institute, National Institutes of Health, USPHS (CA-07470), The American Cancer Society (P-68), The National Science Foundation (GB-6616X), and The Damon Runyon Fund for Cancer Research (DRG-920).

Allan L. Goldstein is the recipient of a Career Scientist Award of the Health Research Council of the City of New York under Contract I-519.

REFERENCES

ALEXANDER, J. W. and GOOD, R. A. (1970) *Immunobiology for Surgeons.* Philadelphia: Saunders.

ARCHER, O. K. and PIERCE, J. C. (1961) *Fedn Proc. Fedn Am. Socs exp. Biol.* **20,** 26.

ASANUMA, Y., GOLDSTEIN, A. L. and WHITE, A. (1970) *Endocrinology* **86,** 600.

CLAMEN, H. N., CHAPERON, E. A. and TRIPLETT, R. F. (1966) *Proc. Soc exp. Biol. Med.* **122,** 1167.

COHEN, M. W., THORBECKE, G. J., HOCHWALD, G. M. and JACOBSON, E. B. (1963) *Proc. Soc. exp. Biol. Med.* **114,** 242.

DIGEORGE, A. M. (1968) In *Immunologic Deficiency Diseases in Man*, ed. Bergsma, D. *Birth Defects*, original article series vol. IV, no. 1, pp. 116–123. New York: National Foundation.

FAHEY, J. L., BARTH, W. F. and LAW, L. W. (1965) *J. natn. Cancer Inst.* **35,** 663.

FORD, C. E. and MICKLEM, H. S. (1963) *Lancet* **1,** 359.

GATTI, R. A., STUTMAN, O. and GOOD, R. A. (1970) *A. Rev. Physiol.* **32,** 529.

GOLDSTEIN, A. L., ASANUMA, Y., BATTISTO, J. R., HARDY, M. A., QUINT, J. and WHITE, A. (1970a) *J. Immun.* **104,** 359.

GOLDSTEIN, A. L., ASANUMA, Y. and WHITE, A. (1970) *Recent Prog. Horm. Res.* **26,** 505.

GOLDSTEIN, A. L., GUHA, A., HOWE, M. L. and WHITE, A. (1970b) *J. Immun.* Submitted for publication.

GOLDSTEIN, A. L., SLATER, F. D. and WHITE, A. (1966) *Proc. natn. Acad. Sci. U.S.A.* **56,** 1010.

GOLDSTEIN, A. L. and WHITE, A. (1970a) In *Biochemical Actions of Hormones*, vol. 1, pp. 465–502, ed. Litwack, G. New York: Academic Press.

GOLDSTEIN, A. L. and WHITE, A. (1970b) In *Current Topics in Experimental Endocrinology*, vol. 1, ed. James, V. H. T. and Martini, L. New York: Academic Press. In press.

GOOD, R. A. (1967) *Hospital Practice* **7,** 39.

GOOD, R. A., DALMASSO, A. P., MARTINEZ, C., ARCHER, O. K., PIERCE, J. C. and PAPERMASTER, B. W. (1962) *J. exp. Med.* **116,** 773.

GOOD, R. A. and GABRIELSON, A. E. (ed.) (1964) *The Thymus in Immunobiology.* New York: Hoeber.

GOWANS, J. L. (1969) *Harvey Lect.* **64**, in press.
GOWANS, J. L. and McGREGOR, D. D. (1965) *Prog. Allergy* **9**, 1.
HESS, M. W. (1968) *Experimental Thymectomy, Possibilities and Limitations.* New York: Springer-Verlag.
HUMPHREY, J. H., PARROTT, D. M. V. and EAST, J. (1964) *Immunology* **7**, 419.
JERNE, H. K. and NORDIN, A. A. (1963) *Science* **140**, 405.
LAW, L. W., GOLDSTEIN, A. L. and WHITE, A. (1968) *Nature, Lond.* **219**, 1391.
MILLER, J. F. A. P. (1961) *Lancet* **2**, 748.
MILLER, J. F. A. P. (1967) *Modern Trends in Pathology* **2**, 140.
MILLER, J. F. A. P. and MITCHELL, G. F. (1968) *J. exp. Med.* **128**, 801.
MILLER, J. F. A. P. and OSOBA, D. (1967) *Physiol. Rev.* **47**, 437.
MILLER, J. F. A. P., TING, R. C. and LAW, L. W. (1964) *Proc. Soc. exp. Biol. Med.* **116**, 323.
MITCHELL, G. F. and MILLER, J. F. A. P. (1968) *J. exp. Med.* **128**, 821.
OSOBA, D. and MILLER, J. F. A. P. (1964) *J. exp. Med.* **119**, 177.
RYGAARD, J. (1969) *Acta path. microbiol. scand.* **77**, 761.
SALVIN, S. B., PETERSON, R. D. A. and GOOD, R. A. (1965) *J. Lab. clin. Med.* **65**, 1004.
SIMONSEN, M. (1962) *Prog. Allergy* **6**, 349.
STUTMAN, O., YUNIS, E. J. and GOOD, R. A. (1969) *J. natn. Cancer Inst.* **41**, 1431.
TRAININ, N., BEJERANO, A., STRAHILEVITCH, M., GOLDRING, D. and SMALL, M. (1966) *Israel J. med. Sci.* **2**, 549.
TRAININ, N., BURGER, M. and KAYE, A. (1967) *Biochem. Pharmacol.* **16**, 711.
WHITE, A. and GOLDSTEIN, A. L. (1970a) *Ciba Fdn Symp. Control Processes in Multicellular Organisms*, pp. 210–237. London: Churchill.
WHITE, A. and GOLDSTEIN, A. L. (1970b) In *Immunogenicity*, ed. Borek, F. Amsterdam: North-Holland. In press.
ZISBLATT, M., GOLDSTEIN, A. L., LILLY, F. and WHITE, A. (1970) *Proc. natn. Acad. Sci. U.S.A.* **66**, 1170.

DISCUSSION

Bloch: Is there any indication that your calf thymus extract is species specific in its activity?

A. White: No; but at the moment the only data we have to the contrary are the following. An antiserum has been prepared to calf thymosin, using Freund's adjuvant, in rabbits (Hardy *et al.* 1969). This antiserum cross-reacts with thymocytes and peripheral lymphoid cells from the calf, as judged by cytotoxicity and agglutination studies *in vitro*. Rather surprising has been the observation that this antiserum to calf thymosin also cross-reacts with mouse and rabbit thymocytes, but not significantly with mouse and rabbit peripheral lymphoid cells. In our thymosin preparation, there may be a thymus-specific antigen. However, there is no evidence that such an antigen can function to reconstitute the deficiencies of a neonatally thymectomized animal.

We have also administered calf thymosin for several weeks to normal CBA mice, and there is no evidence of refractoriness developing to the material.

Sorkin: Are you able to titrate the concentration of thymosin in the circulation?

A. White: We have not yet done the necessary experiments to establish whether thymosin fulfils an essential criterion to be designated as a hormone, by demonstrating its presence in the blood. We are at present developing a radioimmunological assay which we hope will help answer your question.

King: When you incubate thymosin with spleen cells and then re-inject these cells into an animal in which they are immunologically active, can you tell from the quantitative aspects whether this is a specific absorption of thymosin to the cells, and so you are putting thymosin into the animal, or do you think the spleen cells are making more thymosin?

A. White: Your question is very appropriate. We haven't done the critical control experiment; that is, we have not incubated thymosin with non-lymphoid cells, and then put these cells into an animal to see whether our data may reflect an action of thymosin absorbed to the injected cells. However, the likelihood of this being the case is not very great, in view of the fact that the amount of thymosin administered in these circumstances would not be very large. We are incubating 10^7 cells with 100 μg or, in some cases, 10 μg or 1 μg of thymosin, and injecting 5×10^6 of these cells. We do know that administration of 1 μg of thymosin to a lethally irradiated animal does not cause proliferation of the remaining lymphoid cells of the spleen.

King: You are thinking then in terms of thymosin having an active effect on the cells *in vitro*?

A. White: We are hypothesizing that thymosin accelerates the immunological maturation of cells which would eventually become mature with time.

Owen: I would like to bring up the question of whether you are really activating stem cells. I am thinking particularly of the work of Old, Boyse and their colleagues (Boyse and Old 1969), who have shown that in mice there are at least two differentiation steps involved in the formation of thymus-derived lymphocytes.

The first step is the differentiation, within the thymus, of stem cells of bone marrow origin into thymus lymphocytes. This step involves an extensive change in surface structure since the alloantigens θ, TL, Ly-A and Ly-B are not present on the surface of marrow stem cells but they are expressed on thymus lymphocytes. The second step is the differentiation of thymus lymphocytes to peripheral (thymus-derived) lymphocytes and this also is accompanied by remodelling of the cell surface, involving complete loss of TL and a decrease in θ, Ly-A and Ly-B.

I feel that your experiments can be interpreted in a number of ways. While thymosin may influence either or both of these differentiation steps, it is equally likely that it influences neither but simply stimulates proliferation of the few thymus-derived cells left in your experimental animals.

A. White: With regard to stem cells, one of our studies has been on the rate of regeneration of lymphoid tissue in mice treated with thymosin after lethal X-irradiation (Goldstein *et al.* 1970). Adult mice were irradiated with 700 R and then given 4 mg of thymosin protein within two hours after irradiation and then 4 mg daily for two successive days. The animals were injected with 10 μC of [³H]thymidine or [³H]deoxycytidine 70·5 hours after irradiation and killed at 72 hours. Animals treated with thymosin showed a remarkably greater rate, more than a 100 per cent over controls, of regeneration of lymphoid tissue as measured by incorporation of isotope into peripheral lymph node DNA. Radioautographs of lymph node sections reveal labelling of cells almost entirely in the more primitive stem cell series which are developing in the regenerating lymph nodes. There is very little, if any, isotope discernible in the small, more mature lymphocytes. These findings may, in part, answer your question.

We have adopted the general thesis that, in contrast to adrenal steroids, which Dougherty and I showed (1945) to be particularly effective in causing lymphocytokaryorrhexis of small lymphocytes and to a lesser degree of medium and larger lymphocytes, thymosin may be functioning as the other component of a homeostatic mechanism, accelerating the maturation of more primitive cells derived from a stem cell population. We do not know whether thymosin acts at the initial stem cell locus or at a later stage of lymphoid cell differentiation.

Lance: Dr White and Dr Goldstein were good enough to supply four coded fractions, one of which was thymosin, to Dr Robert Taub and myself. We studied these fractions in two different systems: in the first we administered equal quantities of each fraction to groups of CBA mice and measured the rate of incorporation of ^{125}I-labelled 5-iodo-2′-deoxyuridine (IUDR) in the recipient lymph nodes, spleen and thymus. This study was designed to see whether one of the fractions had a specific effect on lymphoid tissue, causing cell division and rapid proliferation. We found that all four fractions caused an increased incorporation of IUDR into the lymphoid organs under study and no significant differences were observed between them. We were forced to conclude that this effect was non-specific and related to the immunogenicity of the heterogeneous proteins. It is, however, possible that a specific effect may have been masked in these circumstances.

In the second system, we examined the ability of the four fractions to alter the numbers of recirculating lymphocytes in normal mice or to hasten the recovery of recirculating lymphocytes in thymectomized mice treated with antilymphocyte serum. In this latter system, we adopted the dosages and timings used by Monaco and his co-workers (Franco *et al.* 1970). We were unable to demonstrate any effect of any of these fractions on the rate of recovery of recirculating lymphocytes in these circumstances.

A. White: We have as yet had no experience in our laboratory on the effect of thymosin on the output of thoracic duct lymphocytes in normal adult or thymectomized mice treated with ALS. However, in experiments with Dr Lloyd Law (Law, Goldstein and White 1968) we observed an increased level of blood lymphocytes in neonatally thymectomized mice given thymosin. We have confirmed this observation recently (Asanuma, Goldstein and White 1970).

Humphrey: An obvious question is whether with thymosin you can switch cells from one compartment to another.

Fachet: Have you ever studied the effect of thymosin on the thymus itself in the normal animal? Are there any feedback mechanisms here?

A. White: Yes, I believe so. It is striking that if one gives thymosin to a normal mouse the one tissue which is smaller than in normal, untreated mice is the thymus. Only in the lethally irradiated animal, in which the thymus has been markedly in-voluted, can we demonstrate some proliferative action of thymosin on the thymus. We interpret this in terms of current endocrino-logical concepts, namely that thymosin could be exerting a feedback influence on the thymus in the normal animal.

REFERENCES

ASANUMA, Y., GOLDSTEIN, A. L. and WHITE, A. (1970) *Endocrinology* **86,** 600.

BOYSE, E. A. and OLD, L. J. (1969) *A. Rev. Genet.* **3,** 269.

DOUGHERTY, T. F. and WHITE, A. (1945) *Am. J. Anat.* **77,** 81.

FRANCO, D. J., QUINT, J., HARDY, M. A., GRAY, H. M. and MONACO, A. P. (1970) In *Pharmacologic Treatment in Organ and Tissue Transplantation*, pp. 165–170, ed. Bertelli, A. and Monaco, A. P. Amsterdam: Excerpta Medica Foundation. (International Congress series No. 197.)

GOLDSTEIN, A. L., BANERJEE, S., SCHNEEBLI, G. L., DOUGHERTY, T. F. and WHITE, A. (1970) *Radiat. Res.* **41,** 579.

HARDY, M. A., QUINT, J., GOLDSTEIN, A. L., WHITE, A., STATE, D. and BATTISTO, J. R. (1969) *Proc. Soc. exp. Biol. Med.* **130,** 214.

LAW, L. W., GOLDSTEIN, A. L. and WHITE, A. (1968) *Nature, Lond.* **219,** 1391.

CONFERMENT OF IMMUNOCOMPETENCE ON LYMPHOID CELLS BY A THYMIC HUMORAL FACTOR

Nathan Trainin and Myra Small

Department of Experimental Biology, Weizmann Institute of Science, Rehovoth, Israel

Surgical removal of the thymus soon after birth either hampers or arrests the development of immunological competence in mammals. A syndrome of thymic deficit develops, characterized by atrophy of lymphoid tissues, failure in homograft and delayed hypersensitivity reactions, and impairment of the antibody response to certain antigens (Miller 1961; Good *et al*. 1962; Martinez *et al*. 1962; Arnason, Jankovic and Waksman 1962). In addition to these symptoms, wasting disease sometimes develops, leading to the death of the deprived animals (Parrott 1962; Aisenberg, Wilkes and Waksman 1962).

Most aspects of the immunological damage resulting from neonatal thymectomy can be reversed by implanting neonatal thymus grafts (Dalmasso *et al*. 1963; East and Parrott 1964). The question was therefore asked whether this organ acts as a source of competent cells which seed peripheral lymphoid organs, or whether its main activity involves the production of a humoral factor which participates in the process leading to immunological maturation of cells produced elsewhere. Experiments in which thymic grafts enclosed in cell-impermeable diffusion chambers were implanted in thymectomized recipients indicated the possible existence of a humoral mechanism, since most of the defects following neonatal thymectomy could be prevented by this procedure (Levey, Trainin and Law 1963; Osoba and Miller 1963; Law *et al*. 1964; Aisenberg and Wilkes 1965; Trench *et al*. 1966).

On the basis of these early experiments, we adopted as a working hypothesis the concept that thymus function is non-cellular in nature, and oriented our efforts towards identifying a humoral factor responsible for thymus activity. After repeated administration of crude extracts from mouse, rabbit, sheep and calf thymuses to intact and thymectomized mice, we observed an increase in the lymphocyte population of the peripheral blood and the lymphoid organs. When administered to neonatally thymectomized mice, these extracts also prevented wasting disease (Trainin *et al.* 1966). These parameters were of a rather non-specific nature, however, and a clearer indication of repair of thymic function was required. It was considered desirable, therefore, to evaluate the efficiency of thymus extracts vis-à-vis those immunological deficits induced in newborn mice by thymectomy, and in adult mice by the combination of thymectomy and irradiation. Indeed, as shown in Table I, restoration of the immunological reactivity of neonatally thymectomized mice to tumour homografts followed repeated injection with calf thymus extracts (Trainin and Linker-Israeli 1967; Trainin, Burger and Linker-Israeli 1967). As seen in Table I, this reparative effect was obtained even under such conditions as those created when the challenging tumour was of the same H-2 histocompatibility locus as the thymectomized recipient. (SWR mice were challenged with a transplantable C57Bl/6 fibrosarcoma, both strains sharing the same H-2b locus.) It was also demonstrated later that repeated injections of these calf thymus preparations into thymectomized mice led to partial restoration of their ability to form antibodies in a primary response against sheep erythrocytes (Small and Trainin 1967).

Also, in these early series of "*in vivo*" experiments, we were able to show that repeated injections of calf thymus extracts restored the impaired capacity of spleen cells from neonatally thymectomized donor mice to induce a graft-versus-host reaction in appropriate F_1 hybrid recipients (Simonsen's graft-versus-host assay). Fig. 1 shows one of these experiments, indicating that spleen cells from newborn thymectomized donors, injected twice weekly for 10 weeks with calf thymus extracts, induced splenomegaly with significantly higher spleen indices in the recipient mice than that produced by cells from thymectomized controls (Trainin and Linker-Israeli 1967). This preliminary set of experiments strengthened the postulate that at least some of the functions of the thymus are mediated by a humoral mechanism.

The application of *in vitro* techniques to this problem enabled us to seek answers to a number of unsolved fundamental questions,

TABLE I

RESTORATION OF IMMUNOLOGICAL REACTIVITY TO ALLOGENEIC TUMOUR GRAFTS BY REPEATED INJECTIONS OF CALF THYMUS EXTRACTS INTO NEONATALLY THYMECTOMIZED MICE

Treatment of recipients	Lethal takes/number of mice grafted		Percentage of lethal takes	
	C57Bl/6*	SWR/Jax**	C57Bl/6*	SWR/Jax**
Intact controls	0/15	0/9	0	0
Thymectomy	7/15	5/6	47	83
Thymectomy + calf kidney extract†	—	5/6	0	83
Thymectomy + calf thymus extract†	0/14	2/8	0	25

*C57Bl/6 mice were thymectomized within 24 hours after birth and challenged intramuscularly with a C3H fibrosarcoma at 12 weeks of age.

**SWR/Jax mice were thymectomized at 3 days of age and challenged intramuscularly with a C57Bl fibrosarcoma at 16 weeks of age.

†Organ extracts were injected twice weekly beginning at 2 to 3 weeks of age.

such as: is the restoration of immunocompetence of thymectomized recipients after injection with thymus preparations the
result of a non-specific antigenic stimulation induced by repeated
injection of foreign material, or can restoration also be attained
by syngeneic extracts? Does the cell-free component of thymus
tissue exert a direct effect on target cells? Is the effect of thymus
extract achieved by activating existing cells, or does it trigger

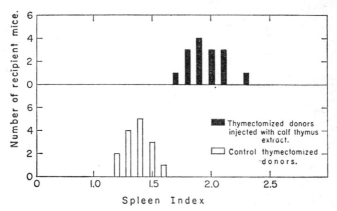

FIG. 1. The effect of injecting calf thymus extract into neonatally thymectomized C57Bl/6 mice on restoration of
immunological reactivity of their spleen cells, measured by
the graft-versus-host response against (C57Bl/6 × C3H/eb)F$_1$
recipients.

them to divide and proliferate until a new and different cell
population is established? Is the ability to restore the immunological reactivity of neonatally thymectomized animals specific
to thymus extracts, or is it shared by extracts obtained from other
components of the lymphopoietic system? What is the chemical
nature of the active principle of thymus preparations? And
finally, what is the identity of those target cells activated by the
thymus humoral factor, and what is the nature of this activation?
The *in vitro* graft-versus-host procedure of Auerbach and
Globerson (1966) seemed to us to be an assay of immunocompetence appropriate to clarifying these questions.

It was necessary, as a first step, to show whether the failure of
spleen cells from neonatally thymectomized mice to evoke a

2*

graft-versus-host reaction when injected into genetically appropriate recipients could be reproduced in *in vitro* conditions. Spleen cells from young adult C57Bl/6 mice were tested for their capacity to induce enlargement of a spleen explant from a newborn (C3H × C57Bl)F$_1$ hybrid *in vitro*, as compared with a paired explant challenged with syngeneic F$_1$ spleen cells. As seen in Fig. 2, 1 × 10^6 or 0·5 × 10^6 spleen cells from intact donors pro-

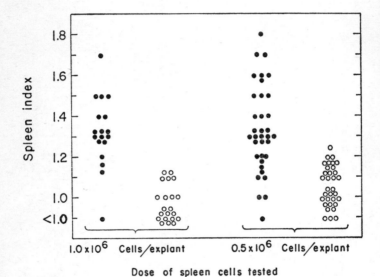

FIG. 2. Graft-versus-host response induced *in vitro* by spleen cells from intact or neonatally thymectomized C57Bl/6 mice. Spleen explants from newborn (C3H/eb × C57Bl/6)F$_1$ mice were challenged by dissociated spleen cells from intact (●) or neonatally thymectomized (○) donors. Each point represents one culture.

duced, in the majority of cultures, a positive graft-versus-host response, with a spleen index of 1·2 or higher, these cultures therefore being considered as reactive. On the other hand, an equivalent number of parental cells from thymectomized donors did not produce splenomegaly, thus expressing their impaired immunological competence (Trainin, Small and Globerson 1969).

We then investigated the possibility of activating these incompetent cells by the presence of a thymic humoral factor. Thymic extract was prepared from thymuses of young adult C57Bl/6 mice (see Materials and Methods in Trainin, Small and Globerson 1969), and added, at a concentration of 2 per cent, to the regular culture medium used in these *in vitro* experiments. After 4–5 days, the usual period of observation, it was possible to observe that the presence of thymus extract restored to the spleen cells of thymectomized C57Bl/6 mice their impaired capacity to induce splenomegaly in F_1 explants. These experiments, summarized in Table II, led us to the following conclusions: (a) that spleen cells from thymectomized mice could attain immunological competence *in vitro* under the influence of a non-cellular component of the thymus; (b) that this restoration is not the result of a mere non-specific antigenic stimulation, since the thymus extracts and cells tested were syngeneic; (c) that this endowment of immunological competence was specifically linked to thymus extracts, since extracts of other components of the lymphoid system, such as spleen and mesenteric lymph nodes, tested at the same protein concentration as the thymus extracts, did not repair the damage that neonatal thymectomy caused to lymphoid cells; and (d) that this influence of thymus extract on lymphoid cells is the result of a direct interaction on the cells, since the experimental conditions excluded the possibility of an indirect mechanism.

The next step was to incubate dissociated spleen cells from thymectomized donors with thymus extracts before these cells were used to challenge the F_1 spleen explants. The aim of this test was to study whether thymus extracts could restore the impaired immunological competence of lymphoid cells prior to the antigenic stimulation created by the conditions of the assay. Spleen cells from thymectomized donors were incubated at 37 °C in culture medium containing thymus extract, and after 1 hour the cells were removed from the shaking water bath and washed before being added to spleen explants to test their ability to induce a graft-versus-host reaction. The results of three different experiments are presented in Fig. 3. It can be seen that a significant percentage of reactive cultures was obtained when spleen cells from thymectomized donors were incubated in thymus extract, whereas aliquots of the same cells exposed to spleen or lymph

TABLE II

GRAFT-VERSUS-HOST RESPONSE INDUCED *IN VITRO* BY SPLEEN CELLS FROM NEONATALLY THYMECTOMIZED C57BL/6 MICE IN THE PRESENCE OF SYNGENEIC THYMUS, SPLEEN, OR MESENTERIC LYMPH NODE EXTRACT

Extract tested*	Incidence of reactive cultures**				Percentage of cultures responding
Thymus	3/5	9/10	3/4	4/5	79·0
Spleen	0/4	1/5	0/4	1/6	10·5
Mesenteric lymph node	0/5	2/10	1/5		15·0
	1/4	1/5	0/4	0/6	10·5

*Syngeneic extracts were tested at a concentration of 0·02 g protein/100 ml culture medium throughout the 4-day assay.
**Number of cultures with a spleen index ≥ 1·2/total number of cultures tested. Each column represents one experiment in which spleen cells from the same donor mouse were tested against newborn (C3H/eb × C57Bl/6)F₁ spleen explants.

node extracts or to culture medium did not show any significant sign of reactivation. The rapidity of this restoration suggests that the activating effect of the thymus factor is exerted upon target cells already present in the culture, rather than by stimulating proliferation of new populations of cells. Both the nature of this activation and the identity of the particular lymphoid cells affected are still unknown.

Further experiments were performed to determine whether the capacity to confer immunocompetence is species-specific

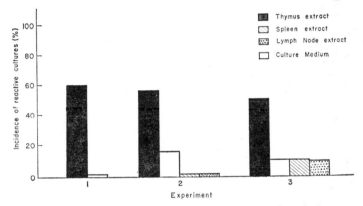

FIG. 3. Graft-versus-host response induced *in vitro* by spleen cells from neonatally thymectomized C57Bl/6 mice preincubated for 1 hour in syngeneic thymic, spleen or mesenteric lymph node extract. Cultures with spleen index of $\geqslant 1 \cdot 2$ are considered reactive.

or whether, as suggested by previous *in vivo* experiments, a thymus factor may still be active across the barrier of strain and species. Thymus extracts were prepared in the same way as before from various strains of mice and from calves. These allogeneic and xenogeneic thymus preparations were tested on C57Bl/6 lymphoid cells from thymectomized mice and evaluated by the same graft-versus-host assay. As seen in Table III, thymus extracts prepared from C3H, SWR or (C3H × C57Bl/)F₁ mice, or from calves, conferred upon defective cells from thymectomized C57Bl/6 mice the ability to react against F₁ explants. Spleen extracts from the same sources tested at the same protein concentration failed to induce significant splenomegaly.

TABLE III

GRAFT-VERSUS-HOST RESPONSE INDUCED *IN VITRO* BY SPLEEN CELLS FROM NEONATALLY THYMECTOMIZED C57BL/6 MICE IN THE PRESENCE OF ALLOGENEIC OR XENOGENEIC THYMUS OR SPLEEN EXTRACT

Extract tested*		Incidence of reactive cultures**					Percentage of cultures responding
Species	Organ						
(C3H × C57Bl)F₁ mouse	Thymus	4/5	2/5	4/10			50
	Spleen	0/5	0/5	0/10			0
C3H/eb mouse	Thymus	2/4	3/5	5/10			53
	Spleen	0/5	0/5	0/10			0
SWR mouse	Thymus	4/5	3/5	5/10			60
	Spleen	1/5	0/5	1/10			10
Calf	Thymus	4/4	6/7	5/9	5/5	4/7	75
	Spleen	0/5	1/7	0/9			5

*Extracts were tested at a concentration of 0·02 g protein/100 ml culture medium throughout the 4-day assay.
**Number of cultures with a spleen index $\geq$ 1·2/total number of cultures tested.

Experiments were then oriented towards determining some of the physicochemical properties of the active principle in xenogeneic thymus preparations. The first procedures chosen were dialysis and ultrafiltration of the supernatant of crude thymus extracts. As seen in Fig. 4, it was found that the active factor passes through cellophane dialysis sac No. 27/32 (Union Carbide, U.S.A.) and also through cellophane dialysis tubing No. 23/32 during exhaustive dialysis. Since the active fraction of the thymus

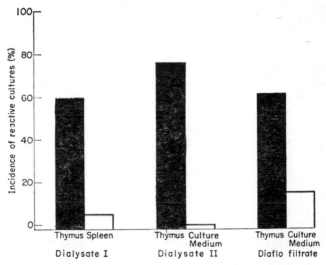

FIG. 4. Restoration of graft-versus-host reactivity in spleen cells from neonatally thymectomized C57Bl/6 mice by fractions prepared from calf thymus extract. Fractions obtained by dialysis through cellophane dialysis sac No. 27/32 (I), dialysis through cellophane dialysis sac No. 23/32 (II), and by Diaflo ultrafiltration were tested in the 4-day assay. Cultures with spleen index of $\geqslant 1 \cdot 2$ are considered reactive.

extract was recovered in the dialysate in both cases, the active principle would appear to be a molecule of less than 6000 molecular weight. Ultrafiltration by Diaflo membranes was then carried out, and it was possible to recover the active principle in filtrates passing through Diaflo UM-2 membranes, indicating that the molecular weight of the active factor is of the order of magnitude of 1000 or less. Further experiments are in progress in our laboratory to determine other physicochemical properties of this factor, with the aim of defining its chemical nature and structure.

All the experiments described were done with lymphoid cell populations manifesting an impaired immunological competence as a result of neonatal thymectomy. It seemed to us of interest, in addition, to determine whether the thymus humoral factor has some measurable effect on populations of lymphoid cells from intact mice. In order to detect an increase in immune reactivity in cell populations from intact mice, inocula of 1×10^5 spleen cells were tested, since they were found to contain insufficient numbers of competent cells to induce, on their own, a graft-versus-host reaction. As seen in Table IV, when thymus extracts were added *in vitro* either to suspensions of spleen cells or to fragments of spleen tissue from which cell suspensions were subsequently tested, the presence of this extract did not increase the competence of these spleen cell populations to a level detectable by initiation of a graft-versus-host reaction. However, when cell inocula obtained from intact mice previously injected *in vivo* (18 to 24 hours before testing) with thymus extracts were tested by the usual *in vitro* graft-versus-host assay, it was found that 1×10^5 spleen cells attained the capacity to initiate a graft-versus-host response. These results were obtained after injecting calf thymus extract or syngeneic thymus preparations. Since an assay performed with cell suspensions prepared 2 hours after injection of calf thymus extract gave a less consistent effect, these experiments suggest that *in vivo* injection of the thymus humoral factor into intact mice produces a gradual increase in the proportion of competent cells within the spleen, this increase being the expression of the influence of the thymus factor on target cells originating outside the spleen.

At this time we have demonstrated that the active principle of thymus extracts which confers immunocompetence upon lymphoid cells is probably a molecule of an order of magnitude of 1000 or less. This principle seems to be common to various species of mammals, and its chemical nature is currently under investigation. The interaction between the active principle of thymus and its target cells can be observed *in vitro*, but questions

TABLE IV

GRAFT-VERSUS-HOST RESPONSE INDUCED *IN VITRO* BY SPLEEN CELLS FROM INTACT C57BL/6 MICE EXPOSED TO CALF THYMUS EXTRACT

Conditions of exposure	Number of cells tested	Incidence of reactive cultures	Response	
			Percentage of cultures responding	Number of donor mice responding
—	1×10^6	3/3 3/4 4/4 4/4 3/3 4/4 4/4	95	
—	1×10^5	0/4 1/6 1/5 1/5 0/4 1/5	14	
Calf thymus extract present during GVH assay *in vitro*	1×10^5	1/6 2/6 2/6 1/4	27	
Incubation of spleen explants with calf thymus extract for 18–24 hours *in vitro*	1×10^5	0/5 0/9 0/6 0/5	0	
Injection of calf thymus extract 18–24 hours previously	1×10^5	4/6 4/7 5/7 3/4 3/4 2/5 3/5		6/7
Injection of syngeneic thymus extract 18–24 hours previously	1×10^5	4/4 2/5 3/6 4/7 4/6		4/5
Injection of calf thymus extract 2 hours previously	1×10^5	1/4 0/4 4/6 0/4 3/4 3/4 0/5 2/5		3/8

such as the nature of this interaction, the identity of the target cells, and the role of the thymus humoral factor under natural conditions, remain to be answered.

SUMMARY

A humoral factor of the thymus has been shown to reverse many aspects of the immunological damage resulting from neonatal thymectomy. The active principle of thymus extract seems to participate directly in the chain of events leading to immunological reactivity of lymphoid cells, since dissociated spleen cells from neonatally thymectomized mice attained the capacity to initiate a graft-versus-host response when exposed to syngeneic, allogeneic or xenogeneic thymic extracts *in vitro*. Incubation of incompetent lymphoid spleen cells in thymus extracts restored their immunological activity, the rapidity of this restoration suggesting that the effect of the thymus factor is exerted upon cells already present in the culture. Injection of thymus extract into intact mice increases the proportion of competent lymphoid cells in the spleen, possibly by activating target cells produced elsewhere in the body. Results of dialysis and ultrafiltration indicate that the active principle is of a molecular weight of approximately 1000 or less.

REFERENCES

AISENBERG, A. C. and WILKES, B. (1965) *Nature, Lond.* **205**, 716–717.

AISENBERG, A. C., WILKES, B. and WAKSMAN, B. H. (1962) *J. exp. Med.* **116**, 759–772.

ARNASON, B. G., JANKOVIC, B. D. and WAKSMAN, B. H. (1962) *Nature, Lond.* **194**, 99–100.

AUERBACH, R. and GLOBERSON, A. (1966) *Expl Cell Res.* **42**, 31–41.

DALMASSO, A. P., MARTINEZ, C., SJODIN, K. and GOOD, R. A. (1963) *J. exp. Med.* **118**, 1089–1109.

EAST, J. and PARROTT, D. M. V. (1964) *J. natn. Cancer Inst.* **33**, 673–690.

GOOD, R. A., DALMASSO, A. P., MARTINEZ, C., ARCHER, O. K., PIERCE, J. C. and PAPERMASTER, B. W. (1962) *J. exp. Med.* **116**, 773–796.

LAW, L. W., TRAININ, N., LEVEY, R. H. and BARTH, W. H. (1964) *Science* **143**, 1049–1051.

LEVEY, R. H., TRAININ, N. and LAW, L. W. (1963) *J. natn. Cancer Inst.* **31**, 199–205.

MARTINEZ, C., KERSEY, J., PAPERMASTER, B. W. and GOOD, R. A. (1962) *Proc. Soc. exp. Biol. Med.* **109**, 193–196.

MILLER, J. F. A. P. (1961) *Lancet* **2**, 748–749.

Osoba, D. and Miller, J. F. A. P. (1963) *Nature, Lond.* **199**, 653–656.

Parrott, D. M. V. (1962) *Transplantn Bull.* **29**, 102–104.

Small, M. and Trainin, N. (1967) *Nature, Lond.* **216**, 377–379.

Trainin, N., Bejerano, A., Strahilevitch, M., Goldring, D. and Small, M. (1966) *Israel J. med. Sci.* **2**, 549–559.

Trainin, N., Burger, M. and Linker-Israeli, M. (1967) In *Advances in Transplantation* (Proc. I Int. Congr. Transplantation Society), pp. 91–95, ed. Dausset, J., Hamburger, J. and Mathé, G. Copenhagen: Munksgaard.

Trainin, N. and Linker-Israeli, M. (1967) *Cancer Res.* **27**, 309–313.

Trainin, N., Small, M. and Globerson, A. (1969) *J. exp. Med.* **130**, 765–776.

Trench, C. A. H., Watson, J. W., Walker, F. C., Gardner, P. S. and Green, C. A. (1966) *Immunology* **10**, 187–191.

DISCUSSION

Korner: Dr Trainin, are you using the same material as Dr Goldstein and Dr White? Is it reasonable that American thymosin should be sixty times as big as Israeli thymosin? Is your material labile to proteolytic enzymes, for example, as theirs is?

Trainin: We are now studying these parameters. Our preliminary results suggest that our material is of a nucleic acid nature, from the ultraviolet absorption of the material. We have also begun to study it by paper chromatography and we have found already that one of the fractions eluted is highly active. But these are very preliminary results.

Humphrey: Professor White, are you sure you are dealing with the same *phenomena*, even though the extracts seem to be chemically different?

A. White: The phenomena which Dr Trainin reports for his material are very much like what we are seeing with our preparations. However, it must be emphasized that neither laboratory has a physically and chemically pure material as yet. We do, at one stage of our preparation, subject our material to a heat step. Even the highly purified material is, for a protein, relatively heat stable. Neither DNA nor RNA is present in our most purified preparation, and its activity is not altered by incubation with either DNase or RNase, but is lost on digestion with proteolytic enzymes. Our material does not dialyse significantly over a period of time, for example over 24 hours. Moreover, we have tested dialysates of thymosin-containing fractions in neonatally thymectomized mice, and these have been inactive. Of course, conditions of dialysis must be precisely defined; it is conceivable that our active material on dialysis may adhere to the dialysis membrane and not pass to the exterior fluid.

Dr Trainin, you have described your preparation as probably being nucleic acid-like; this is the most significant difference from our material. There are reports that nucleic acids and nucleic acid fragments may cause lymphoid cell proliferation. Is it possible that your end-point of assay responds generally to nucleic acids or partial degradation products of nucleic acids? Also, have you ruled out the possible presence in your dialysates of endotoxin, which in your assay system might cause cell stimulation?

Trainin: We have repeated our *in vitro* experiments with two polynucleotides, poly A and poly AU, instead of thymus extracts, and over the range of concentrations tested we did not find a positive graft-versus-host response. As to the possible participation of endotoxin, since syngeneic thymus extract prepared under aseptic conditions was shown to be active, we might assume that endotoxin is not involved in our system.

Goldstein: This is a very interesting assay for looking at thymic humoral influences. Have you ruled out the possibility that what you have is not a GVH reaction as you see *in vivo*, but rather the stimulation of proliferation by thymic fractions of lymphoid cells *in vitro* over the four-day period of incubation?

Trainin: We have ruled this out because the same thymus extract does not have this influence on F_1 cells. Furthermore, cell suspensions from thymectomized mice previously injected with thymus extracts were capable of inducing a graft-versus-host reaction *in vivo*.

Korner: Are your methods of extraction similar to those used by Dr White and Dr Goldstein? Dr White said that his material aggregates. Do you have a heat step and if so, does it intensify aggregation?

Trainin: Our mouse or calf thymus extracts were prepared in $0 \cdot 1$ M-sodium phosphate buffer pH $7 \cdot 4$. After homogenization of the tissue, mouse preparations were centrifuged at 35 000 **g** for 30 minutes while the calf homogenate was centrifuged for 20 minutes at 2500 **g** and the supernatant centrifuged at 100 000 **g** for either 1 or 5 hours. Both mouse and calf extracts were diluted to contain 10 mg protein/ml as determined by the biuret reaction, and sterilized through Millipore filters of $0 \cdot 45$ μm porosity.

Dialysis of the 100 000 **g** supernatant was performed against a twenty times greater volume of phosphate buffer, 0·005 M, for 60 hours at 5 °C. The dialysate was lyophilized to a dry powder which was redissolved in water. Ultrafiltration of the dialysate was done with a Diaflo-UM2 membrane. As you see, our procedure did not include heating.

A. White: In our opinion at the present time, our thymosin fraction does not aggregate as a result of the heat step. Thus, if we omit the heat step in our fractionation, the subsequent fraction isolated appears similar in properties to that derived from the procedure which includes a heat step.

Pierpaoli: Dr Trainin, might the physicochemical characteristics of the incubation medium, when you add extracts made from different organs, be different, and therefore these might non-specifically influence cell migration and tissue growth during a four-day incubation period? It should be remembered that the thymus is extremely rich in nucleic acid and it has been shown, for example by Braun and his collaborators (1968) and Johnson and co-workers (1968), that oligonucleotides strongly influence the immune response when injected into mice at a defined time after antigenic challenge. Also purely physical parameters, such as the viscosity of the incubation medium, may differ, so that cells may more easily migrate, causing an enlargement of the spleen explant.

Korner: The intriguing point about Dr Trainin's nucleic acid-like material is that if it is true that the molecular weight is less than a thousand, the component must be a nucleotide; it could even be cyclic AMP, or something of that size.

Trainin: When we tried cyclic AMP *in vitro* we did not see the same type of reaction. We *have* tried poly A and poly AU alone, Dr Pierpaoli, and they seem rather negative, as I said earlier. Secondly, it does not seem likely to us that migration of cells influences a graft-versus-host response *in vitro*.

Humphrey: It seems clear that the material of both groups can restore, to stem cells presumably, at least partly those functions which the thymus itself is able to influence. At one stage I thought Dr White was going to suggest that this might be by putting on a coating of the sort of antigenic markers which thymus cells have been shown to have, and which are associated with ability to migrate into the thymus-dependent areas, but this seems now not a likely explanation?

Goldstein: Dr J. Kruger, Dr B. H. Waksman and I (1970) have attempted to see whether thymosin could put a surface antigen on bone marrow cells in adult thymectomized, lethally irradiated rats given syngeneic bone marrow cells. Our results were negative. It appears as though thymosin acts by inducing the rapid maturation of a more primitive cell so that it can respond immunologically, and that this cell has the capacity to recognize an antigen later on. It appears to be more a derepression type of phenomenon, rather than addition of a thymic antigen, which may only determine whether or not the cell can return to the thymus.

Owen: I think there is some confusion about what type of cell we are calling a stem cell. If we are talking about the cell which in both embryonic and adult life migrates to the thymus and becomes a thymus lymphocyte (Ford 1966; Moore and Owen 1967) then I don't think you could conclude from your experiments, Dr Goldstein, that you are activating that cell, simply because in the systems you have looked at, thymus-derived lymphocytes will be present. Thus in neonatally thymectomized mice, thymus-derived lymphocytes are, for a time, present in peripheral lymphoid tissues (Schlesinger and Yron 1970) and in lethally irradiated, bone-marrow-restored mice, the donor bone marrow may contain a few thymus-derived lymphocytes. So thymosin may be acting on cells which have already been processed within the thymus and have migrated to peripheral lymphoid tissues.

Goldstein: More accurately the cells should be described as thymus-dependent cells, and a specific *class* of thymus-dependent cells. It is possible that in the embryonic state many of these cells which have perhaps migrated from the thymus are in the stem cell populations elsewhere, and that the role of thymosin and other thymic factors may be to activate this type of cell. We shall later present our current working hypothesis which will illustrate this point (see General Discussion, pp. 154–157).

Humphrey: One of the advantages of having Dr Trainin and Dr White in the same room is that they might be able to arrange to look at each other's materials using each other's system.

A. White: This would be very desirable. There is the possibility, of course, that there is more than one biologically active thymic principle.

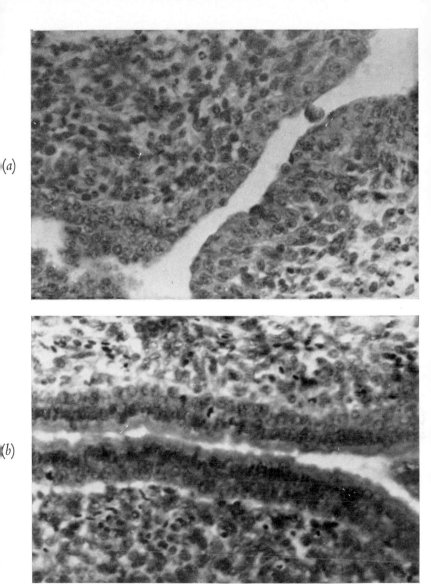

FIG. 1. The bursa "anlage" from 15-day-old chick embryos.
(a) Normal. (b) Testosterone-treated embryo.

(Facing p. 43)

INFLUENCE OF TESTOSTERONE ON THE PRIMARY LYMPHOID ORGANS OF THE CHICKEN

A. SZENBERG

On leave from the Walter and Eliza Hall Institute,
*Royal Melbourne Hospital, Melbourne**

THE immunological role of the thymus and the bursa of Fabricius as primary lymphoid organs of the chicken has been firmly established. The thymus is responsible for the development of specific cell-mediated immune responsiveness, whereas the bursa is indispensable for the development of circulating antibody-producing cells. The experimental findings have been adequately reviewed (Warner and Szenberg 1964; Szenberg and Warner 1967; Warner 1967). The thymus "anlage" in the six-day-old embryo is a purely epithelial structure. The lymphoid development starts between the seventh and the ninth day and at hatching the thymus is fully lymphoidal and functional. In the bursa the epithelial nodules are clearly visible at the fourteenth day of incubation and they become lymphoidal between the sixteenth and eighteenth day. At hatching (21 days) the bursa is fully lymphoidal and probably fully functional.

The lymphoid cells in both the thymus and the bursa originate from haemopoietic blood-borne stem cells which migrate into the epithelial organ "anlage" from the yolk sac. This has been shown clearly by the elegant experiments of Owen and his colleagues (Moore and Owen 1967; Owen and Ritter 1969). Selye in 1943 reported that several androgenic hormones could induce bursal involution. Meyer, Rao and Aspinall (1959) used 19-nortestosterone in chick embryos to prevent the development of the bursa of Fabricius. This method has been further studied by Warner and Burnet (1961). An adequate dose (about 2 mg per embryo) of 19-nortestosterone given to the chick embryo at any time between the fifth and twelfth day of incubation will totally or partially prevent the development of epithelial nodules and lymphoid tissue in the bursa. Forty per cent of

*Present address: Immunology Unit, World Health Organization, Geneva.

REFERENCES

BRAUN, W., NAKANO, M., JARASKOVA, L., YAJIMA, Y. and JIMINEZ, L. (1968) In *Nucleic Acids in Immunology*, pp. 347–363, ed. Plescia, O. J. and Braun, W. New York: Springer.

FORD, C. E. (1966) *Ciba Fdn Symp. The Thymus: Experimental and Clinical Studies*, pp. 131–152. London: Churchill.

JOHNSON, A. G., SCHMIDTKE, J., MERRITT, K. and HAN, I. (1968) In *Nucleic Acids in Immunology*, pp. 379–385, ed. Plescia, O. J. and Braun, W. New York: Springer.

KRUGER, J., GOLDSTEIN, A. L. and WAKSMAN, B. H. (1970) *Cell. Immun.* **1**, 51.

MOORE, M. A. S. and OWEN, J. J. T. (1967) *J. exp. Med.* **126**, 715.

SCHLESINGER, M. and YRON, I. (1970) *J. Immun.* **104**, 798.

chickens hatched from hormone-treated embryos will not produce a detectable antibody response, even after repeated stimulations (Warner et al. 1969).

If the hormone is given early, at five or six days of incubation, the anatomical structure of the bursa will not develop. If the hormone is applied later, at nine to twelve days, the anatomical structure of the bursa will exist but will be empty of lymphoid tissue. In about 40 per cent of such treated embryos the thymus development is also suppressed, in 30 per cent partially, and in 10 per cent of cases totally (Szenberg and Warner 1962). The important question is whether the suppressive action of the hormone treatment is directed against the epithelial part of the primary lymphoid organs or against the lymphocytes or both.

In the bursa of Fabricius morphological observations indicate that under the influence of the hormone the normal, at this stage cubical type of epithelium of the bursa "anlage" and of the cloaca prematurely differentiate into the cylindrical, secretory type of epithelium of the adult cloaca (see Fig. 1). It cannot be shown directly that this early differentiation of the epithelium is the reason why it loses its other functions, namely the stimulation of local lymphopoiesis and induction of differentiation of haemopoietic stem cells into immunocytes, but it seems to be the reasonable explanation (Warner and Burnet 1961; Szenberg, unpublished observations). Another interesting observation is that even in cases where the hormonal bursectomy was total —that is, the bursal structure cannot be seen—still large numbers of plasma cells can be seen directly under the epithelial layer of the cloaca. This would indicate that some remnants of the specific inductive qualities of the epithelial tissue of this area may still have remained intact. This would also explain the findings that even in bursectomized chickens with no detectable antibody response, a certain level of immunoglobulins may still be present in the circulation (Carey and Warner 1964; Warner et al. 1969).

If the hormone acted directly on the haemopoietic stem cells, the frequency with which the thymus was also affected should have paralleled the action on the bursa. However, the level of circulating lymphocytes in bursectomized chickens is normal, which indicates that the supply of stem cells to the thymus has not been impaired. Experiments with anti-growth hormone serum in mice (Pierpaoli and Sorkin 1968) show that such serum will induce thymic atrophy in adult and young mice, and wasting syndrome in young animals, a similar effect to neonatal thymectomy, namely removal of the epithelial part of this organ. No wasting is induced by anti-growth hormone serum in adult animals, which again indicates that the deprivation of the growth hormone greatly influences the activity of the epithelial part of the thymus. In adult birds the thymus persists as an atrophic organ, but can undergo seasonal reactivation (Höhn 1956). This reactivation can be induced experimentally by large doses of thyroxine (Höhn 1959; Warner 1964). The restoration of normal morphology in the thymus of such birds indicates reactivation of the epithelial structure of this organ. The observation of Ernström (1965) that the lymphatic hyperplasia which can be induced by thyroxine in young adult guinea pigs does not appear in thymectomized animals, points in the same direction.

CONCLUSIONS AND SUMMARY

The evidence presented indicates that testosterone prevents or suppresses the development of primary lymphoid organs in the chicken by acting directly on the epithelial part of these organs. In the bursa this action is accompanied by early differentiation of the epithelial cells into a cylindrical secretory type of epithelium.

The hormone can also have some suppressive activity in young adult birds.

Thyroxine can reactivate epithelial cells in the thymuses of adult birds.

It is quite probable that other hormones, for instance somatotropic (growth) hormone, influence the immune system by acting on epithelial tissue of primary lymphoid organs. The possibility of direct action of the above-mentioned hormones on the lymphoid cells cannot be excluded.

REFERENCES

Carey, J. and Warner, N. L. (1964) Nature, Lond. **203,** 198.
Ernström, U. (1965) Acta path. microbiol. scand. **64,** 83.
Höhn, E. O. (1956) Can. J. Biochem. Physiol. **34,** 90.
Höhn, E. O. (1959) J. Endocr. **19,** 282.
Meyer, R. K., Rao, M. A. and Aspinall, R. L. (1959) Endocrinology, **64,** 890.
Moore, M. A. S. and Owen, J. J. T. (1967) J. exp. Med. **126,** 715.
Owen, J. J. T. and Ritter, M. A. (1969) J. exp. Med. **129,** 431.
Pierpaoli, W. and Sorkin, E. (1968) J. Immun. **101,** 1036.

SELYE, H. (1943) *J. Morph.* **73,** 401.
SZENBERG, A. and WARNER, N. L. (1962) *Nature, Lond.* **194,** 146.
SZENBERG, A. and WARNER, N. L. (1967) *Br. med. Bull.* **23,** 30.
WARNER, N. L. (1964) *Aust. J. exp. Biol. med. Sci.* **42,** 401.
WARNER, N. L. (1967) *Folia biol., Praha* **13,** 1.
WARNER, N. L. and BURNET, F. M. (1961) *Aust. J. biol. Sci.* **14,** 580.
WARNER, N. L. and SZENBERG, A. (1964) *A. Rev. Microbiol.* **18,** 253.
WARNER, N. L., UHR, J. W., THORBECKE, J. G. and OVARY, Z. (1969) *J. Immun.* **103,** 1317.

DISCUSSION

Humphrey: Dr Szenberg has indicated a quite different approach to the mode of action of factors controlling differentiation. May I ask about the fate of the injected nortestosterone? This presumably stays in the embryo at least until hatching; it is a stable compound and the embryo is therefore flooded with hormone. I was wondering whether it would be possible to put into a treated embryo a piece of presumptive bursa which had not been exposed to testosterone, but if the embryo is flooded with the hormone you won't be able to do this.

Szenberg: No, the hormone remains there. Incidentally, shortly after hatching the male chick's own testosterone production starts, indicated by the fact that the size of the bursa is smaller in cocks than in hens.

Owen: In experiments with Malcolm Moore (Moore and Owen 1966) we treated chick embryos of 5 days' incubation with testosterone so that their bursal development was completely inhibited. Bursas from normal 12-day embryos were then grafted to the chorioallantois of treated embryos and were found to show good lymphoid development. Where donor and host were of opposite sex, sex chromosome analysis of dividing cells in these bursas showed that they were populated by lymphoid stem cells of host origin. This clearly shows that the availability of stem cells is not affected by testosterone treatment.

R. G. White: You illustrated the similarity between the organization of the mammalian thymus and the bursa in birds. One marked difference is the presence in the bursa of a ring of epithelial-like cells which separates the medulla (inside) from a basement membrane and the cortex (outside). This ring did not seem to be present after treatment of the embryo with testosterone.

Szenberg: This ring consists of connective tissue and vessels. It is visible at about 18 days. The epithelial cells are located in the centre. After treatment with testosterone the whole structure fails to develop; you just find a little bit of epithelial tissue which escapes hormone action, and around this is some lymphoid tissue development, but the normal structure with demarcated regions is absent.

R. G. White: What is the effect of testosterone on substances such as acid sulphated mucopolysaccharides? Are they eliminated from the bursa?

Szenberg: The epithelial cells of the bursa "anlage" are absent if the hormonal bursectomy has been successful, so we cannot answer the question about the direct influence of the hormone on the production of acid mucopolysaccharide. On the other hand, the normal mucus production of the mature cloacal endothelium starts at 19 to 20 days of incubation and this mucus also gives a positive staining reaction with PAS.

Korner: Dr Szenberg, do you know any biochemical changes which are associated with the effects of androgens in preventing development of the epithelium of the bursa?

Szenberg: No.

A. White: As I mentioned earlier (p. 21), in the mouse, rat and rabbit, corticosteroids destroy the more mature, small lymphoid cells. What interests me in relation to Dr Szenberg's presentation is that testosterone is known also to reduce the size of lymphoid tissue in the mouse (cf. Dougherty 1952). We have in the past been of the opinion, and perhaps incorrectly, that the action of testosterone is also an effect on lymphoid elements rather than on the reticular epithelial cells. Dr Szenberg, have you done experiments in the mouse? In the chicken you have a nice dissociation between the primary locus of action of the two kinds of steroids, androgens acting on the epithelial cells and oestrogens on lymphoid cells. Secondly, large doses of oestrogens will cause lymphoid tissue proliferation in mice (Gardner, Dougherty and Williams 1944). Do oestrogens affect the lymphoid cells in the chick embryo? If the effect was proliferative this might explain why the female of many species generally responds more rapidly with humoral antibody synthesis after challenge with antigen than does the male.

Szenberg: Once we had got the effect on the chicken the obvious thing was to try it in the mouse, to produce a thymusless mouse by giving testosterone to the pregnant mother. There was no effect, probably because the mother can metabolize the injected hormone before it affects the embryos. So I cannot tell if you can prevent development of the thymus in the mouse hormonally, unless you could find some way to give testosterone directly to the embryo.

Secondly, you are really asking whether I think that testosterone acts *only* on the epithelial part of the bursa. I have no proof of any other effect, but I couldn't exclude by our experiments that testosterone does not have some action on lymphoid cells.

A. White: It would be possible to put testosterone directly into the thymus of the mouse embryo; carcinogenic hydrocarbons have been instilled directly into the thymus of mice (Stutman, Yunis, and Good 1969).

Szenberg: Selye (1943) found that oestrogens also have a depressive, specific action on the development of the primary lymphoid organs in the chicken, not as strong and not as constant as testosterone.

A. White: The effect will depend on the dose of oestrogen. Low doses cause non-specific ACTH release from the pituitary and one may therefore see the involutionary effects of adrenal steroids on lymphoid tissue. However, as I indicated, large doses of oestrogens will lead to lymphoid tissue hypertrophy.

Fachet: Dr White mentioned the difference between the actions of corticosteroids and testosterone on lymphatic tissues. In this respect, we have injected corticosteroids into rats and puppies 24 hours after birth (Fachet *et al.* 1966, 1967). They developed a condition which resembles the wasting syndrome that follows neonatal thymectomy in rats (Fachet, Palkovits and Vallent 1965). A single injection of either 0·5 mg or 1 mg of cortisol given to newborn rats impaired the development of the thymus and thymus-dependent lymphoid system and suppressed the cellular and humoral immune responses (Fachet, Stark and Palkovits 1968).

King: On the question of whether androgen is acting directly or indirectly on the thymus, neonatal injection of androgen switches off the hypothalamic mechanism that controls the oestrous cycle in females. This leads to a state of constant oestrus. Do you know whether any of the hypothalamic or pituitary factors evoke the same response as androgen in your system?

Szenberg: No, we have not tried that.

Bloch: Can you say something further about the regeneration of the epithelial cells of the thymus in the adult chicken by thyroxine?

Szenberg: If you give to an adult bird, which has an atrophied thymus, large doses of thyroxine (2 mg per day for 14 days) the thymus reverts to the normal structure of the young thymus. Whatever the epithelial part of the thymus is producing is produced again, since the normal morphology of the cortex is restored.

Fabris: Have you tried to prevent the atrophy caused by injecting testosterone into chick embryos by giving thyroxine?

Szenberg: No, we haven't. The dose of 2 mg per day that you would have to use to get an effect would kill the embryo. However, maybe we should try with smaller doses of thyroxine, although I suspect it will not prevent atrophy, since the action of thyroid hormones must come after the anlage has developed.

A. White: I am not familiar with the effects of thyroxine on lymphoid tissue following its involution by testosterone. However, after injection of adrenal steroids into mice, or in the regeneration of lymphoid tissue after irradiation, thyroxine will accelerate regeneration of lymphoid tissue (unpublished results). The thyroid–adrenal cortical relationship may constitute one homeostatic system for regulation of lymphoid tissue structure and function.

Pierpaoli: A few years ago we did some experiments to test whether sexual maturation would influence the lymphatic tissue and the immunological capacity of neonatally thymectomized mice (Pierpaoli and Sorkin 1968). These experiments were based on the observation that neonatal thymectomy in mice produces cytological changes in the hypophysis and that these modifications are particularly evident at the time of sexual maturation (Pierpaoli and Sorkin 1967).

We found that gonadectomy before puberty in neonatally thymectomized male or female mice produces a complete reconstitution of the structure and morphology of the peripheral lymphatic tissues but not of their capacity to form antibody against sheep erythrocytes. It would seem therefore that either we have removed target cells in the thymus which could be under the regulation of some hormones, possibly somatotropic hormone, and which produce a specific thymus factor responsible for the differentiation of antibody-forming cells, or we have simply prevented, by gonadectomy, hormones which antagonize the action of developmental hormones from acting on the lymphatic tissues when sexual maturation occurs.

In spite of the fact that chickens and mammals are at least a few million years apart in terms of phylogenetic evolution, I think that the action exerted by developmental hormones in both species is very similar if not identical. We have perhaps to distinguish between the action of a hormone in the differentiation of cells that have been prepared by their genetic pattern for a specific hormonal action to take place, and the actual performance of hormones acting on a mature lymphoid system. It seems that the experiments performed by Dr Szenberg show an action of the first kind, before the formation of a particular type of mature lymphoid tissue.

Gunn: Sherman and Dameshek (1963) demonstrated the profound influence of the sex of the animal on wasting after neonatal thymectomy. In hamsters the males wasted and the females did not and this difference, absolute if thymectomy was performed during the first three days of life, was still detectable if thymectomy was performed up to the end of the first month. Sherman, Adner and Dameshek (1963) extended these observations and were able to demonstrate that in neonatally thymectomized male hamsters orchidectomy or administration of oestrogenic hormones prevented wasting and in neonatally thymectomized females oophorectomy or administration of testosterone permitted wasting.

Fachet: Professor Dameshek told me he was not able to repeat this finding of a sex difference in the incidence of wasting after neonatal thymectomy in hamsters.

Gunn: I don't know of confirmation by other groups of the situation in hamsters but certainly the reports by Sherman and his colleagues were very convincing. However, Balner and Dersjant (1966) have demonstrated that in certain strains of mice there is a sex difference in immune depression and runting after neonatal thymectomy. Again the male is more at risk than the female and the difference can be potentiated or eliminated by appropriate endocrine ablation or hormone therapy.

Fachet: In this connexion, our experiments in progress show that after high (50 mg/100 g body weight) doses of cortisone in young adult thymectomized CBA mice, there is a higher incidence of the fatal ''wasting syndrome'' in males than in similarly treated (same dose per 100 g body weight) female young adult thymectomized mice (J. Fachet and D. M. V. Parrott, unpublished observations 1970).

Sorkin: Concerning the wasting disease after neonatal thymectomy, an interesting sex difference has been observed by Osoba (1965). Whereas unmated thymectomized female CBA mice died of wasting disease before the 15th week of age, parous females were still seemingly healthy at more than 17 weeks of age. The protective effect of pregnancy was, however, not permanent (Elders, Parham and Hughes 1968).

Owen: Dr Szenberg, did you imply that the timing of administration of testosterone is not very critical? You said that testosterone injected early in development completely inhibits the formation of the bursa, but if it is injected later in incubation a remnant of bursa may be found. Timing in that sense seems to be important.

Szenberg: The treatment with testosterone at 6 to 8 days of incubation will very frequently prevent the development of the anatomical structure of the bursa completely. If the hormone is applied at 9 to 12 days of incubation quite often the morphological structure of the bursa will develop but the formation of the epithelial part of the bursa, the bursa ''anlage'', can still be prevented. This happens in about 60 per cent of the treated embryos. It is not the absence of the stem cells which prevents the development of the lymphoidal structure of the bursa because at this stage of incubation (12 days) they are still circulating in the embryo, but they do not settle in the bursa if the epithelial ''anlage'' has not developed.

Humphrey: Is there an embryological reason why one particular bit of the gut epithelium, the bursa, should have this inductive action but not the epithelium of the adjacent parts of the gut? Is this due to some basic developmental reason or is it an anatomical accident?

Owen: It may not just be the epithelium that is important; Auerbach (1960) showed that an interaction between epithelium and mesenchyme is crucial for the formation of the thymic anlage. A similar interaction may be necessary for the formation of the bursa, since Ackerman and Knouff (1963) have shown that testosterone inhibits alkaline phosphatase activity in the mesenchyme of the developing bursa and they have suggested that this inhibition secondarily affects the formation of lympho-epithelial nodules.

Korner: Can one reverse the effects of the androgen with inhibitors of nucleic acid or protein biosynthesis?

Owen: I don't think this has been attempted. Dr Szenberg, do you think that there may be several levels at which testosterone may act in the system? For instance, it may act on mesenchyme or epithelium at early stages of bursal development; on the other hand it might act by killing maturing lymphoid cells within the bursa at later stages?

Szenberg: If you give testosterone to a newly hatched chick you can still depress growth of the bursa but I feel that it is not just killing of the lymphoid cells, because testosterone given at that time produces a smaller final bursal development, not a depletion of lymphoid cells in a normal-sized bursa. Even at this late stage with large doses you can suppress the activity of the epithelium, so that full development of the organ is prevented. The problem of whether large doses of testosterone also act on lymphoid cells is unresolved, though I suspect that they do.

Pierpaoli: The effects of any hormone should be considered in conjunction with the action of other hormones which may either antagonize it or act synergistically with it. For example, we were able to reconstitute the depressed immune capacity of cortisol-treated mice and to reconstitute their involuted lymphatic tissue with somatotropic hormone (Fabris, Pierpaoli and Sorkin 1970). Therefore it is conceivable that testosterone given at that stage of development to chickens acts not only directly on the lymphoid cells or their precursors but may antagonize the effect of the developmental hormone which would produce a second step of the lymphoid tissue development. Probably a very delicate homeostatic regulation of the precursors of the cells of the immunolymphatic tissue exists once these precursors have been adequately prepared for the hormonal action by the gene-dictated transformation.

Szenberg: I don't know about the whole system; I think we can exclude, by Dr Owen's experiments and some of our own observations, an influence on the supply of stem cells, which appears normal in the testosterone-treated embryos. If, for instance, you get hormonal bursectomy with a normal thymus, you find a completely normal turnover and number of circulating lymphocytes. The supply of stem cells into the thymus therefore has not been inhibited by the hormonal treatment. So I think the action is not at this level. However, there still could be several other levels at which the hormone can act to produce the final effect of preventing the development of the epithelial tissue, but we cannot yet tell what they are.

Pierpaoli: Do you think, however, that this is strongly indicative of a very early development of a lymphoid cell compartmentation, based on different sensitivities to developmental hormones?

Szenberg: Yes.

REFERENCES

ACKERMAN, G. A. and KNOUFF, R. A. (1963) *Anat. Rec.* **146,** 23.

AUERBACH, R. (1960) *Devl Biol.* **2,** 271.

BALNER, H. and DERSJANT, H. (1966) *Nature, Lond.* **209,** 815.

DOUGHERTY, T. F. (1952) *Physiol. Rev.* **32,** 379.

ELDERS, M. J., PARHAM, B. A. and HUGHES, E. R. (1968) *J. exp. Med.* **127,** 649.

FABRIS, N., PIERPAOLI, W. and SORKIN, E. (1970) In *Developmental Aspects of Antibody Formation and Structure.* Prague: Publishing House of the Czechoslovak Academy of Sciences. In press.

FACHET, J., PALKOVITS, M. and VALLENT, K. (1965) *Acta med. hung.* **21,** 305.

FACHET, J., PALKOVITS, M., VALLENT, K. and STARK, E. (1966) *Acta endocr., Copenh.* **51,** 71.

FACHET, J., STARK, E. and PALKOVITS, M. (1968) *Acta med. hung.* **25,** 395.

FACHET, J., STARK, E., PALKOVITS, M. and VALLENT, K. (1967) *Gen. Comp. Endocr.* **9,** 449.

GARDNER, W. U., DOUGHERTY, T. F. and WILLIAMS, W. T. (1944) *Cancer Res.* **4,** 73.

MOORE, M. A. S. and OWEN, J. J. T. (1966) *Devl Biol.* **14,** 40.

OSOBA, D. (1965) *Science,* **147,** 298.

PIERPAOLI, W. and SORKIN, E. (1967) *Br. J. exp. Path.* **48,** 627–631.

PIERPAOLI, W. and SORKIN, E. (1968) *Br. J. exp. Path.* **49,** 288–293.

SELYE, H. (1943) *J. Morph.* **73,** 401–421.

SHERMAN, J. D., ADNER, M. M. and DAMESHEK, W. (1963) *Blood* **22,** 252.

SHERMAN, J. D. and DAMESHEK, W. (1963) *Nature, Lond.* **197,** 469.

STUTMAN, O., YUNIS, E. J. and GOOD, R. A. (1969) *J. natn. Cancer Inst.* **41,** 1431.

HORMONAL INFLUENCES ON THYMIC RELEASE OF LYMPHOCYTES INTO THE BLOOD

U. ERNSTRÖM

Department of Histology, Karolinska Institutet, Stockholm, Sweden

IN our laboratory we have been studying the thymus–lymphatic system of the guinea pig. During the last five years we have concentrated on the migration of cells between different parts of the lymphatic system. Our studies have also included the influences of hormones on the production and migration of lymphocytes.

Before discussing the influence of steroids on the thymic release of lymphocytes, I shall describe our technique and some of our results in normal animals. The guinea pig has a cervical thymus which makes possible surgical procedures and measurements that are not easily made in animals with an intrathoracic thymus. As in the human newborn, the lymphoid system of the guinea pig is very mature at birth. Nevertheless, it is possible to show morphological defects in neonatally thymectomized guinea pigs (Ernström 1965). The number of lymphocytes in the blood is decreased (Ernström and Larsson 1966). The shortage is most pronounced among the small lymphocytes—those which we characterize by a low content of mitochondria.

These findings made us interested in the export of lymphocytes from the thymus. This export could be quantified by comparing the cellular content of afferent and efferent thymic blood. We found a very significant venous–arterial difference in the number of lymphocytes. In male guinea pigs, 1–2 months old, about 700 thymic lymphocytes are added to each μl of blood passing through the thymus. A subdivision of the lymphocytes into different categories proved that the difference was made up mainly of small lymphocytes (629 ± 167 per μl). Thus, the significant release of lymphocytes from the thymus consisted exclusively of small lymphocytes (Ernström and Larsson 1967).

To make a more detailed estimate of the export we measured the flow of blood through the thymus in the following way. The thymic veins empty into the internal jugular vein. The jugular vein was ligated proximally and distally to the confluence of the thymic veins, as were all other small veins except the thymic veins. A heparinized polyethylene catheter was introduced through a minor incision in the wall of the jugular vein. The blood flow from the thymus was led to a small container placed on a precision balance on which continuous readings of the flow of blood were made. A constant flow for 20 minutes was required. The wound was covered with liquid paraffin at 35 °C. By this technique the blood flow from each thymic lobe was determined to be 41 μl per minute (Larsson 1966), giving a total of 82 μl per minute for both thymic lobes. From this figure and the venous-arterial difference in the number of lymphocytes, the thymic export of lymphocytes could be calculated. The thymus releases $82 \times 629 = 5 \cdot 2 \times 10^4$ small lymphocytes per minute, or $7 \cdot 4 \times 10^7$ small lymphocytes per 24 hours.

The investigations were continued with a study of the export of newly produced lymphocytes from the thymus. Guinea pigs were labelled by an intraperitoneal injection of [³H]thymidine. The thymic venous–arterial difference in the number of lympho-cytes was measured. The percentage of labelled lymphocytes was obtained by radioautography of blood smears. The results proved that most labelled lymphocytes were released from the thymus 2 and 3 days after having synthesized DNA and divided. With repeated injections of [³H]thymidine we showed that almost all lymphocytes were labelled when released from the thymus 3 days later (Ernström and Larsson 1969).

This and other experiments have shown that the small lympho-cytes in the thymus are exchanged in about 3 days. This informa-tion makes it possible to calculate the ratio between exported lymphocytes and the total production of lymphocytes in the thymus. In our guinea pigs, which weigh about 250 g, 27 per cent of the lymphocytes are released into the blood and the re-maining 73 per cent either die inside the thymus or leave the thymus by lymphatic vessels (Ernström and Sandberg 1970).

INFLUENCE OF STEROIDS ON OUTPUT OF LYMPHOCYTES FROM THE THYMUS

Guinea pigs were given a single intraperitoneal injection of a thymolytic steroid (prednisolone, 50 mg/kg body weight) and were studied at different intervals after the injection. During the first 6 hours the number of small lymphocytes circulating in the blood and lymph was normal or above normal. At 1, 3, 6 and 9 days after the steroid injection the number of circulating small lymphocytes was markedly decreased both in the blood and in thoracic duct lymph (Fig. 1). In thymectomized guinea pigs, the steroid-induced deficiency in small lymphocytes in the blood occurred earlier, 3 hours after the steroid injection.

The influence of steroids on the thymic release of lymphocytes was studied by estimating the number of lymphocytes in thymic afferent and efferent blood (Ernström and Larsson 1967) and by measuring the thymic blood flow (Larsson 1967). Soon after giving the steroid the venous-arterial difference in the number of small lymphocytes was about normal, but between 1 and 9 days after the injection the difference decreased to 20 per cent of the normal value (Fig. 2). At the same time more large lymphocytes were found in the thymic afferent blood than in the efferent blood. These findings indicate a greatly diminished export of small lymphocytes from the thymus and a flow of large lymphocytes into the thymus.

By determining the blood flow through the thymus it was possible to quantify the release of cells from the thymus during steroid-induced involution and regeneration. Surprisingly, the flow of blood passing through the thymus soon after the steroid injection was about twice the normal flow. After 24 hours the blood flow became normal (Fig. 3).

The release of cells from the thymus per minute was calculated (Fig. 3). During the first 6 hours after injection of prednisolone the release of small lymphocytes was increased above the normal level. At 24 hours and later, the release was markedly decreased.

This investigation was continued with an examination of the thymic export of labelled lymphocytes two days after the incorporation of [³H]thymidine. The export of labelled lymphocytes was normal 3 and 6 hours after the steroid injection. After 24 hours the export was decreased to about 50 per cent and after 3, 6 and 9 days no export of labelled lymphocytes was detected. After 6 days there was in fact a flow of labelled lymphocytes *into* the thymus (Larsson 1967).

The decreased release of small lymphocytes from the thymus after treatment with steroids may be due to decreased

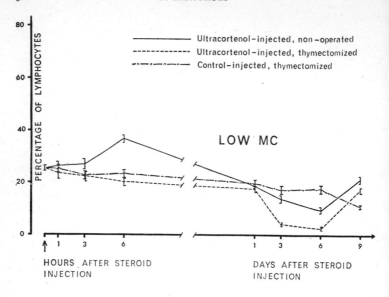

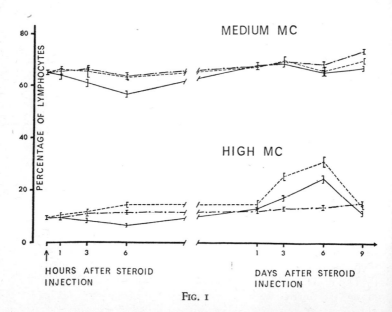

Fig. 1

DNA synthesis and cellular proliferation and may also be due to increased lysis of thymic lymphocytes *in situ*.

The effect of steroids on the thymic release of lymphocytes can be summarized as follows. During the first hours after the injection of a steroid increased numbers of small lymphocytes are released from the thymus. This prevents an immediate fall in the number of blood lymphocytes. At 24 hours and later the release of small lymphocytes from the thymus is markedly decreased and at the same time the number of circulating small lymphocytes decreases.

During the regeneration of the lymphatic tissue after steroid involution, an increased number of large lymphocytes appear in the blood and in the lymphoid tissue. Some of the circulating large lymphocytes migrate into the thymus. They may contribute to thymic regeneration.

We have also applied a similar technique to the spleen. The splenic venous-arterial difference in the number of lymphocytes was determined. We found a higher number of lymphocytes in efferent than in afferent blood, indicating that lymphocytes were also released from the spleen. However, this difference was less than in the thymus and consisted of lymphocytes of all categories, in contrast to the exclusive export of small lymphocytes from the thymus. The thymic export is essentially unaffected by immunization but the splenic export can be increased, for example during the response to pertussis antigens (Ernström and Sandberg 1968).

The influence of steroids on the splenic release of lymphocytes has also been investigated. Prednisolone caused a slightly increased venous-arterial difference after 24 hours, irrespective of thymectomy. No steroid-induced decrease of the splenic export was found (Ernström, Gyllensten and Sandberg 1969). This is

FIG. 1. Percentage of lymphocytes with different mitochondrial content (MC) in thoracic duct lymph of guinea pigs after treatment with prednisolone (Ultracortenol). The arrow indicates thymectomy and injection of steroid.

The figure demonstrates that the steroid-induced deficiency in small lymphocytes is not restricted to the blood but also occurs in the lymph. The combination of thymectomy and steroid treatment causes an almost complete absence of the smallest type of lymphocytes after 3 and 6 days.

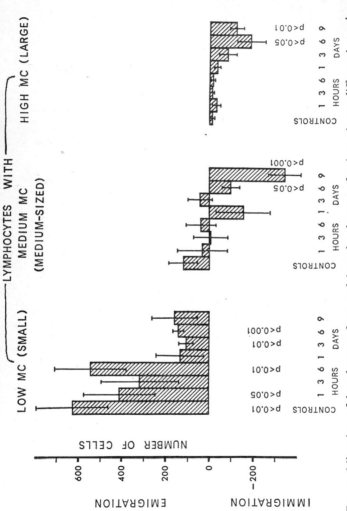

Fig. 2. Migration of lymphocytes from and into the thymus of guinea pigs at different intervals after a single injection of prednisolone (Ultracortenol), determined as the thymic venous-arterial difference in number of cells per μl of blood passing through the thymus. MC, mitochondria.

The figure demonstrates the decreased thymic release of small lymphocytes 1, 3, 6 and 9 days after steroid administration. During the regeneration after the steroid-induced involution an immigration of lymphocytes with medium and high mitochondrial content occurs into the thymus.

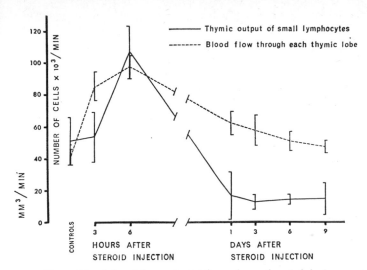

FIG. 3. Blood flow (μl per minute) through one thymic lobe in guinea pigs at different intervals after the administration of prednisolone (Ultracortenol). From the blood flow and the venous–arterial difference in the number of small lymphocytes (Fig. 2), the total release of small lymphocytes from the thymus was calculated per minute.

in contrast to the marked decrease of the thymic release of lymphocytes after steroid treatment.

Thymectomy alone, or in combination with steroid, caused a transitory decrease of the splenic output of small lymphocytes (Ernström, Gyllensten and Sandberg 1969; Ernström and Sandberg 1969). This is in agreement with earlier investigations demonstrating a delayed regeneration of steroid-involuted lymphoid tissue after thymectomy, even when performed in adult animals (Ernström and Gyllensten 1965).

SUMMARY

A considerable export of small lymphocytes can be demonstrated from the thymus of guinea pigs by comparing the lymphocyte content of afferent and efferent thymic blood and by measuring thymic blood flow. Labelling studies with [³H]thymidine

3*

show that the emigrating lymphocytes have synthesized DNA and divided within 3 days before leaving the thymus.

When guinea pigs are given a single injection of a thymolytic steroid (prednisolone), there is a deficiency in the small lymphocytes in the blood, which appears earlier in thymectomized than in intact guinea pigs. The blood flow through the thymus and the export of small lymphocytes from the thymus are increased during the first few hours after the steroid injection. Blood flow later returns to normal and the export of small lymphocytes decreases to 20 per cent of the normal output. During its regeneration large lymphocytes enter the thymus.

REFERENCES

ERNSTRÖM, U. (1965) Acta path. microbiol. scand. 65, 192–202.

ERNSTRÖM, U. and GYLLENSTEN, L. (1965) Acta path. microbiol. scand. 64, 193–202.

ERNSTRÖM, U., GYLLENSTEN, L. and SANDBERG, G. (1969) Acta path. microbiol. scand. 76, 43–51.

ERNSTRÖM, U. and LARSSON, B. (1966) Acta path. microbiol. scand. 67, 267–275.

ERNSTRÖM, U. and LARSSON, B. (1967) Acta path. microbiol. scand. 70, 371–384.

ERNSTRÖM, U. and LARSSON, B. (1969) Nature, Lond. 222, 279–280.

ERNSTRÖM, U. and SANDBERG, G. (1968) Acta path. microbiol. scand. 72, 379–384.

ERNSTRÖM, U. and SANDBERG, G. (1969) Acta path. microbiol. scand. 76, 52–60.

ERNSTRÖM, U. and SANDBERG, G. (1970) Acta path. microbiol. scand. in press.

LARSSON, B. (1966) Acta path. microbiol. scand. 67, 586–587.

LARSSON, B. (1967) Acta path. microbiol. scand. 70, 390–397.

DISCUSSION

Sorkin: You mentioned that there was essentially no change in the release of lymphocytes from the thymus after the injection of antigens. I would have thought that there might be at least a difference between the primary and secondary response, especially perhaps with regard to cellular immunity; the release of thymus-derived cells might be specially affected by an antigenic challenge resulting in cellular immunity, such as a skin graft.

Ernström: I have not investigated the thymic export of lymphocytes during a secondary challenge. However, a single dose of pertussis vaccine causes a continuing response, because the antigen persists in the animal for a long time. After a single injection of pertussis vaccine or of *E. coli* lipopolysaccharide the antibody titre and the blood lymphocyte number fluctuate periodically, but the thymic output of cells changes very little (Ernström and Larsson 1967*a*). During an immune response the increase in the release of lymphocytes is much more pronounced from the spleen than from the thymus (Ernström and Sandberg 1968).

Lance: How long does it take for animals to recover normal levels of thymus output after the injection of corticosteroid in the dose range that you were using? Secondly, have you any data on the kinetics of thymic output after adrenalectomy?

Ernström: The output of cells from the thymus after giving steroid is normal after about 2–3 weeks. I have no data which would answer the question about adrenalectomized animals.

Lance: Why do you think it takes so long for the return to normal after a single pulse of steroids? We have observed this too in our system and are puzzled by it. The effect on the thymus appears to long outlast the known metabolic lifetime of the steroid dose. If you assume that the change is taking place solely within the thymus, it's hard to understand why this should be so, unless there was some other effect as well, maybe on the stem cells?

Ernström: I don't know whether the effect is on the epithelial cells, as Dr Szenberg believes in his experiments with testosterone, as well as on the lymphoid cells.

Lance: The turnover of lymphocytes takes place in three days, according to your labelling experiments, so presumably if the action of steroids that you are measuring was on those cells resident in the thymus, three days later a whole new population would come in and one would expect to see recovery in about three or five days. It sounds as if some antecedent process is also being affected.

Ernström: We cannot exclude the importance of the action of steroids on other lymphoid organs and on the bone marrow, maybe on the proliferation of stem cells. It may be a steroid-induced delay before stem cells reach the thymus. We found an immigration of large lymphocytes into the thymus during the regeneration period 6–9 days after the steroid injection (Ernström and Larsson 1967*b*), and these cells must multiply in the thymus before we get a total regeneration in terms of thymic weight. I don't know if those large lymphocytes are the stem cells.

Humphrey: Is the thymus structurally disorganized by the

steroid? It swells temporarily immediately after giving corticosteroid; after that do you know whether its architecture is disorganized?

Ernström: After giving a steroid of this type and dose we saw a slight disorganization during the first two hours, with the occurrence of dead cells which are phagocytozed by macrophages. Structural regeneration is very rapid and after 24 hours the histological picture is normal, but the thymus is still involuted in terms of its weight.

Trainin: The concept that 95 per cent or more of the thymic cells die off in the thymus was almost axiomatic after Metcalf put forward his interpretation of labelling experiments with thymus-grafted mice (Matsuyama, Wiadrowski and Metcalf 1966). Evidence such as that of Weissman (1967) suggested that thymus cells do migrate. Now Dr Ernström has made this very interesting report of a venous-arterial difference which indicates that 20–30 per cent of the thymus cells are migrating. In the light of your information, should Metcalf's idea be considered obsolete?

Ernström: It may be a species difference. It is not impossible that rats and mice have a smaller release of thymus cells than guinea pigs. The effect of steroids is also different; mice and rats respond very strongly to steroids, and show more marked death of thymic lymphocytes after an injection of steroid. The guinea pig is rather resistant to steroids and does not react as extremely as do rats and mice. I think that one per cent of the thymic cells being released is too low a figure, but I have only my results from the guinea pig to go on, which shows a much greater release of cells from the thymus. My belief is that the released thymic lymphocytes are important in interactions with other cells in the immune response, which is why we did the experiments.

A. White: The dose of steroid used may be a significant factor. The dose of prednisolone which you used was 50 mg/kg given intraperitoneally; this dose in the rat produces very profound alterations in the thymus. I have not had experience with the guinea pig, but in the mouse, rat and rabbit the thymus is the most sensitive of the lymphoid structures to steroid and one effect is to inhibit mitosis of lymphoid cells.

In relation to Dr Lance's question, it is possible that the slow rate of repopulation of lymphoid cells could be a result of acute lymphocytokaryorrhexis in all the lymphoid structures. As a result, the number of lymphocytes being added to the circulation per unit of time is very much depressed. This occurs after giving steroids to mice, rats and rabbits, and is dose dependent. It is rather surprising that the level of blood lymphocytes was maintained in these experiments.

Your data indicating a flushing out of thymocytes possibly related to blood flow, and rather specifically restricted to the thymus, are rather surprising. Did you measure systemic blood pressure?

Ernström: No.

A. White: Steroids of course are in certain circumstances hypertensive. I was surprised that you didn't find an increased rate of blood flow in the submaxillary gland.

Ernström: After the injection of steroid the blood flow through the thymus increased, but the blood flow through the submaxillary gland was still normal. This perhaps indicates that a change in systemic blood pressure is not the cause of the increased thymic blood flow.

As regards the dose of steroid, we chose a small dose which corresponds to a physiologically possible level of the hormone. We had a slight involution of the thymus and a very slight involution of other lymphoid organs. Of course the thymus is the most sensitive target organ for steroids in the guinea pig also.

A. White: With regard to Dr Lance's question, it may not be surprising if there is no relationship between how long the steroid is present and the consequences of its effect. Berliner, Keller and Dougherty (1961) showed that although intravenously administered cortisol is rapidly taken up by the thymus in the mouse, morphological changes are not evident in the thymus until 3 or 4 hours later when significant radioactivity due to cortisol is no longer detectable in this organ.

Lance: That is a good point. The point I was trying to make was this. It appears to us also, and our data fit very nicely with those of Dr Ernström (see our paper, p. 84), that the immature thymocyte is more susceptible to the action of small doses of steroids than the thymocyte at a later stage of maturation. I wondered whether the reason it took so long for the normal export of thymocytes to be re-established was that an even earlier cell form was being affected, before its immigration to the thymus.

A. White: There is inhibition of proliferation in the thymus itself, as a result of inhibition of mitosis resulting from steroid administration.

Lance: That is another possibility. I wondered if we could differentiate between them, but apparently we can't.

A. White: Incidentally, I am quite surprised by the statement that it isn't the small lymphocyte which is primarily affected by the steroid.

Ernström: We also have given [³H]thymidine to guinea pigs after a single injection of steroid, and we obtained a high output of labelled thymus lymphocytes during the first 6 hours after steroid, as in the other experiments; then during the later phase, at 3, 6 and 9 days, instead we had a small input of labelled lymphocytes, indicating a flow of newly proliferated cells into the regenerating thymus.

R. G. White: Is there an increased population of Kurlov cells in the blood leaving the thymus?

Ernström: We did all the experiments I have described here on male guinea pigs which have no Kurlov cells, but we have also looked at Kurlov cells in mature female guinea pigs. There is a release of such cells into the blood from both the thymus and the spleen. No Kurlov cells were found in the thoracic duct lymph (U. Ernström and G. Sandberg, unpublished results).

R. G. White: These findings would be of interest taken alongside the histological evidence that there are very numerous Kurlov cells in what are described as the efferent lymphatics of the thymus.

Humphrey: I wonder if you ought to take more account of the efferent lymphatics of the thymus, because Professor R. Barer and his colleagues (Harris and Templeton 1968) find that they are quite substantial, and drain particular parts of the thymus. They observed histologically a large number of lymphocytes in the efferent lymph. The total output from the thymus could be substantially bigger than the output measured by venous-arterial differences.

This raises the question of what happens to all these cells, if the thymus exports at least 74 million a day and maybe 100 million a day. How do they finish up?

Ernström: We don't know what fraction of released cells are long-lived and what fraction are short-lived, nor how many of the cells contribute to the expansion of the total lymphoid system in the growing guinea pig (1–2 months old).

Szenberg: At the peak of the lymphocyte output after giving cortisol, are the cells viable?

Ernström: We know that they are living, because we study the lymphocytes immediately by supravital staining with neutral red and Janus green B in order to stain the mitochondria. We assess the category of the lymphocytes by the number of mitochondria they contain. Dead cells are easily recognized.

REFERENCES

BERLINER, D. L., KELLER, N. and DOUGHERTY, T. F. (1961) *Endocrinology* **68,** 621.

ERNSTRÖM, U. and LARSSON, B. (1967a) *Acta path. microbiol. scand.* **70,** 549–560.

ERNSTRÖM, U. and LARSSON, B. (1967b) *Acta path. microbiol. scand.* **70,** 371–384.

ERNSTRÖM, U. and SANDBERG, G. (1968) *Acta path. microbiol. scand.* **72,** 379–384.

HARRIS, P. F. and TEMPLETON, W. R. (1968) *Acta anat.* **69,** 366.

MATSUYAMA, M., WIADROWSKI, M. and METCALF, D. (1966) *J. exp. Med.* **123,** 559.

WEISSMAN, I. L. (1967) *J. exp. Med.* **126,** 291.

SYNERGISM BETWEEN CORTISOL AND ANTILYMPHOCYTE SERUM
PART I OBSERVATIONS IN MURINE ALLOGRAFT SYSTEMS

A. GUNN, E. M. LANCE, P. B. MEDAWAR AND S. L. NEHLSEN

National Institute for Medical Research, Mill Hill, London

A RELATIONSHIP between the adrenal glands and lymphatic tissue was first recognized by Thomas Addison (1855), who described hyperplasia of the lymphoid system in patients suffering from adrenal insufficiency.

After the isolation of the adrenal cortical hormones by Kendall their lytic effect on lymphoid tissues was soon recognized (Selye 1946) and cortisol (hydrocortisone; 17-hydroxycorticosterone) was found superior in this respect to cortisone. Indeed for a time adrenal cortical hormones were assayed biologically by their capacity to induce thymic involution in weanling rats, and cytolysis of lymphocytes *in vitro* (see Dougherty 1952; Santísteban and Dougherty 1954).

Corticosteroids of the cortisol type are weak primary suppressants of cell-mediated immunity even in fairly responsive species such as the rabbit (Billingham, Krohn and Medawar 1951a, b; Krohn 1954) and mouse (Medawar and Sparrow 1956). However, Krohn (1954) demonstrated a more potent effect in reversal of the second-set response, a property now exploited clinically.

The effects of adrenalectomy have been less extensively studied, although in mice and rats proliferation of lymphatic tissues including the thymus, which shows increased mitotic activity after adrenalectomy, is well documented (Dougherty 1960).

Levey and Medawar (1966b) found that adrenalectomy did not perceptibly curtail survival of skin allografts exchanged across H-2 barriers in mice but observed that adrenalectomy did curtail the immunosuppressive action of antilymphocyte serum. Krohn (personal communication) has found that in weak systems, for example male to female, adrenalectomy does accelerate rejection of skin grafts.

Antilymphocyte serum is extremely effective in promoting

the survival of skin allografts (see Medawar 1968). Levey and Medawar (1966*b*) showed that 0·5 mg of cortisol once a week could lengthen the mean survival time of murine skin allografts conferred by 1·25 ml of antilymphocyte serum from 50 days to more than 90 days. We now report experiments which amplify those observations and explore further the functional interaction between antilymphocyte serum and the adrenal glands.

MATERIALS AND METHODS

Mice of strains A and CBA were reared in the colony at the National Institute for Medical Research. Antilymphocyte serum was raised and assayed by the methods of Levey and Medawar (1966*a*). The antilymphocyte sera would regularly double or treble the mean survival times of A strain skin grafts on male CBA mice. Rat skin for xenografts in mice was obtained from the inbred August strain maintained at the National Institute for Medical Research. Antilymphocyte scrum was administered subcutaneously, cortisol intraperitoneally and desoxycortone trimethyl acetate or pivalate by subcutaneous injection in four divided doses. Adrenalectomy and thymectomy were carried out by standard surgical techniques. Adrenalectomized mice received 1 mg desoxycortone trimethyl acetate or pivalate once weekly.

RESULTS

Effect of chronic cortisol treatment or adrenalectomy on the immuno-suppressive effect of antilymphocyte serum

Three groups of male CBA mice (*A*, *B* and *C*) received female A strain tail skin grafts on day 0 and 0·4 ml of once absorbed rabbit-anti-mouse antilymphocyte serum on days 2, 4, 6, 8 and 11—a total of 2 ml. On day 14 group *A* underwent bilateral adrenalectomy and group *C* began a course of 0·2 mg cortisol, twice weekly, while group *B* had no further treatment. The results are depicted in Fig. 1 and Table I. The mean survival time for skin grafts in group *B* (antilymphocyte serum only) was 54·5 days, for group *A* (antilymphocyte serum and adrenalectomy), 41·5 days and for group *C* (antilymphocyte serum and chronic cortisol treatment), 67·5 days. It is known from previous experiments that this dose of cortisol alone has no observable effect on the survival of skin allografts. Thus the results indicate a true potentiating effect of cortisol on the immunosuppressive action of antilymphocyte serum. By contrast, adrenalectomy curtails the immunosuppressive action of antilymphocyte serum. These results confirm and extend the observations of Levey and Medawar (1966b).

TABLE I

EFFECT OF CORTISOL OR ADRENALECTOMY ON THE MEAN SURVIVAL TIME OF A STRAIN SKIN GRAFTS ON CBA MICE TREATED WITH ANTILYMPHOCYTE SERUM (ALS)

	Treatment			
Group	ALS	Adrenalectomy	Cortisol	Mean survival time (days)
A	+	+	—	41·5
B	+	—	—	54·5
C	+	—	+	67·5

Skin grafting on day 0. ALS regime, 0·4 ml on days 2, 4, 6, 8 and 11. Adrenalectomy, day 14. Cortisol regime, 0·2 mg twice weekly.

Maintenance by cortisol of immunosuppression induced by antilymphocyte serum

Groups of CBA male mice received A strain skin grafts and were treated as above with 5 × 0·4 ml antilymphocyte serum. Group A received no further treatment; group B received 0·25 ml antilymphocyte serum twice weekly; group C received 0·25 mg cortisol twice weekly. In group A the skin allografts were rejected between 50 and 60 days after the last dose of antilymphocyte serum, confirming the findings of Lance and Medawar (1969). Animals in groups B and C retained their skin grafts almost indefinitely throughout the period when either treatment was maintained, confirming the observations of Levey and Medawar (1966b) and Lance (1968). Thus repeated small doses of cortisol, themselves ineffective in prolonging skin graft survival, were as effective in maintaining a state of immunosuppression induced by antilymphocyte serum as was continued treatment with antilymphocyte serum itself.

A further example of this phenomenon was observed when administration of 0·1 mg cortisol twice weekly to thymectomized

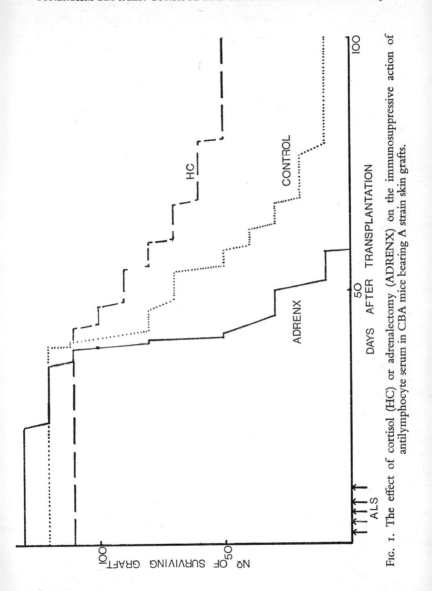

Fig. 1. The effect of cortisol (HC) or adrenalectomy (ADRENX) on the immunosuppressive action of antilymphocyte serum in CBA mice bearing A strain skin grafts.

mice permitted the survival of rat tail skin xenografts on CBA mice for more than three months after the cessation of treatment with antilymphocyte serum.

Potentiation of antilymphocyte serum by prior injection of cortisol

A series of experiments was done in which cortisol in varying dosage was administered prior to a single injection of antilymphocyte serum to CBA mice grafted with A strain skin. The results of a typical experiment are presented in Table II. Cortisol

TABLE II

POTENTIATION OF ACTION OF ANTILYMPHOCYTE SERUM (ALS) ON SKIN GRAFTS BY PRIOR INJECTION OF CORTISOL

Treatment		
Cortisol (dose in μg)	*ALS (dose in ml)*	*Mean survival time (days)*
3 × 200	0·4	26·6
3 × 100	0·4	23·2
3 × 50	0·4	18·2
3 × 0	0·4	17·2
3 × 200	0	12·1
0	0	10·7

Skin grafting A→CBA male mice on day 0. Cortisol on days −1, 0 and +1 (three doses in all). ALS on day +3.

alone in the highest dosage used did not significantly alter the mean survival time. A single injection of antilymphocyte serum alone led to a modest prolongation of skin allograft survival. However, the combination of cortisol and antilymphocyte serum greatly extended the mean survival time, in proportion to the dose of cortisol. The fact that the results obtained with the combination of antilymphocyte serum and cortisol are greater than can be accounted for by simple summation of their individual effects represents true pharmacological synergism.

Interaction of antilymphocyte serum, cortisol and thymectomy

The effect of cortisol with and without thymectomy on the duration of the immunosuppressive state induced by antilympho-cyte serum was explored. CBA mice bearing A strain skin grafts

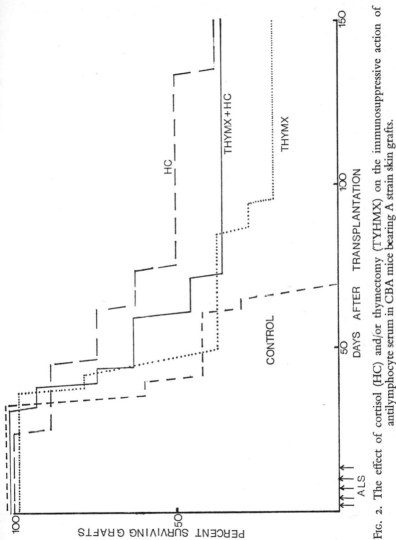

Fig. 2. The effect of cortisol (HC) and/or thymectomy (TYHMX) on the immunosuppressive action of antilymphocyte serum in CBA mice bearing A strain skin grafts.

received 2 ml of antilymphocyte serum in 5 doses, as above. Some of these mice had been thymectomized two or three months before grafting. Those mice receiving cortisol had 0·1 mg twice weekly. Both thymectomy and cortisol administration separately extended the survival time of skin allografts far beyond that achieved with antilymphocyte serum alone. However, the combination of thymectomy and cortisol with antilymphocyte serum was no more effective than either treatment alone with antilymphocyte serum. The results are depicted in Fig. 2.

DISCUSSION

The results of the foregoing experiments demonstrate a remarkable pharmacological synergism between antilymphocyte serum and cortisol on the prolongation of skin allografts in mice. By contrast, adrenalectomy acts by curtailing the immunosuppressive effect of antilymphocyte serum. It is clearly a matter of potential importance that the immunosuppressive effect of antilymphocyte serum as judged by its capacity to permit survival of skin allografts can be maintained by a regular dosage of cortisol which by itself is without observable effect on skin allograft survival, just as effectively as by repeated injection of antilymphocyte serum. This observation needs to be extended, in view of what is known of the undesirability of chronic treatment with antilymphocyte serum.

It emerges clearly from these studies that the effects of cortisol or thymectomy, though either is synergistic with antilymphocyte serum, are not additive, and the inference must be that cortisol acts through the thymus.

The interrelationships of antilymphocyte serum, cortisol, adrenalectomy and thymectomy have been the subject of analysis at a cellular level by Lance and his colleagues and thus form the subject of part II which follows and provide an explanation in cellular terms of the observations described here.

PART II EFFECTS OF CORTISOL AND ANTILYMPHO-CYTE SERUM ON LYMPHOID POPULATIONS

E. M. LANCE AND S. COOPER

Laboratory for Transplantation Immunology, The Hospital for Special Surgery, Cornell University Medical Center, New York

PART I of this report dealt with the functional interrelationship between antilymphocyte serum (ALS) and the adrenal and thymus glands in the context of tissue transplantation. A combination of ALS and cortisol was synergistic in producing and maintaining a state of immunosuppression and a similar augmentation existed when ALS and thymectomy were combined. In the experiments reported below, the changes in lymphoid populations occurring with the various treatment regimens were studied to shed light on the mechanisms of this functional interaction.

Immunosuppressive agents may act on lymphocytes in one of three ways. They may reduce the number of cells below that required for immune rejection (quantitative change). They may interfere with and alter the functional capabilities of the cells (qualitative change); or they may act through a combination of qualitative and quantitative mechanisms. The model we use allows quantitation of changes in lymphoid subpopulations and depends upon the segregation of radio-labelled lymphocytes after their migration when transferred into syngeneic recipients. This method has been used previously for quantitative studies of lymphoid populations (Lance and Taub 1969; Zatz and Lance 1970) and to shed light on the mode of action of antilymphocyte serum (Taub and Lance 1968). The application of this technique under conditions simulating the use of ALS, cortisol and thymectomy in the first portion of this study, suggests that the functional findings may be understood by the quantitative changes which occur in the relevant lymphoid cell populations.

METHODS

Young adult CBA mice obtained from the Jackson Laboratory were used as both cell donors and recipients in all these experiments.

Antilymphocyte serum was raised and assayed by the method of Levey and Medawar (1966a). Such antisera routinely double or treble the mean survival time of A strain skin homografts on CBA male mice. ALS was always administered subcutaneously.

Adrenalectomy and thymectomy were performed by standard surgical techniques and the completeness of extirpation was confirmed at autopsy.

Cortisol was injected intraperitoneally in the form of hydrocortisone acetate. In some experiments, a rapidly excreted preparation (Hydrocortisone hemisuccinate; Solucortef, Upjohn Company) was used.

The technique for measuring the distribution of lymphocytes labelled with chromium-51 in the syngeneic transfer system has been previously described (Lance and Taub 1969). Basically, single cell suspensions are prepared from the lymphoid organs under study and labelled *in vitro* with chromium-51 (Radiochemicals, Amersham). These cells are injected intravenously into panels of syngeneic recipients and 24 hours later the pooled lymph nodes (inguinal, axillary, brachial and mesenteric), spleen and liver of recipients are removed. The accumulated radioactivity is measured in a well-type scintillation counter (Packard–Autogamma). The percentage localization is computed by comparing the number of counts per organ with that found in an aliquot of the original cell suspension. The actual numbers of donor cells localizing in the various organs are determined by multiplying the percentage localization by the number of cells obtained per donor mouse. The results are expressed as the average cell yield, the average percentage localization, and the average number of cells localizing in a given recipient location per donor mouse.

The cells used for these studies were obtained from the lymph nodes of treated animals. In some experiments thymocytes were also studied and are always so specified in the text.

RESULTS

The distribution of normal lymph node lymphocytes

The cell yields and distribution of lymph node cells from untreated CBA males were determined repeatedly during the course of these experiments (usually as concomitant controls). The

TABLE I

DISTRIBUTION OF NORMAL LYMPH NODE CELLS IN SYNGENEIC RECIPIENTS

	Percentage distribution	Number of cells migrating per donor mouse $\times 10^6$	Total cell yield per donor mouse $\times 10^6$
Number of experiments	21	21	24
Lymph node (recirculating population)	13·808 ±2·81	6·206 ±1·839	
Spleen	20·210 =3·116	9·100 ±2·511	42·54 ±10·87
Spleen minus lymph node (non-recirculating population)	6·402	2·894	
Liver	14·147 ±3·927	6·173 ±1·800	

Table II
EFFECTS OF DIFFERENT DOSES OF ALS ON MIGRATION OF LYMPHOID CELLS ON DAY 3

Dose	Percentage distribution				Number of cells migrating per donor mouse $\times 10^6$				Total yield/mouse $\times 10^6$
	Recirculating population	Spleen	Non-recirculating population	Liver	Recirculating population	Spleen	Non-recirculating population	Liver	
0·05 ml ALS	7·9 ±0·3	19·2 ±0·9	11·3	17·7 ±2·6	2·9	7·1	4·2	6·6	34
0·1 ml ALS	6·7 ±0·6	18·8 ±0·3	12·1	19·8 ±2·4	3·9	9·4	5·5	9·9	50
0·25 ml ALS	4·3 ±0·6	17·1 ±2·1	12·8	25·0 ±2·6	1·7	6·8	5·1	10·0	40

TABLE III

RECOVERY FROM TREATMENT WITH ALS

One injection of 0·5 ml ALS per mouse.

Cell yield per donor mouse × 10^6	58·0	36·0	41·0	39·0	37·0
Day	+10	+17	+24	+31	+38
Percentage distribution					
Recirculating } Spleen	2·123 ±0·368	4·164 ±0·79	6·15 ±1·0	8·00 ±2·02	8·35 ±0·87
	15·49 ±1·23	19·87 ±1·1	22·28 ±1·30	20·14 ±3·01	19·83 ±1·55
Non-recirculating } Liver	13·37	15·71	16·13	12·14	11·48
	28·95 ±1·67	23·64 ±2·08	20·66 ±1·61	17·40 ±3·86	15·56 ±1·02
Number of cells migrating					
Recirculating } Spleen	1·05	1·45	1·95	3·35	2·45
	8·9	7·2	9·3	7·8	7·2
Non-recirculating } Liver	7·8	5·7	7·4	4·5	4·7
	16·85	8·6	8·5	6·6	5·6

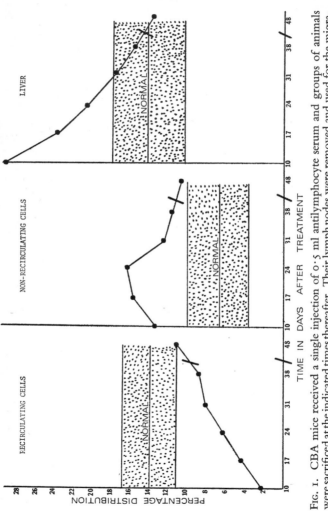

FIG. 1. CBA mice received a single injection of 0·5 ml antilymphocyte serum and groups of animals were sacrificed at the indicated times thereafter. Their lymph nodes were removed and used for the migration assay.

results of 21 separate determinations are shown in Table I and these figures are used throughout to define the limits of normal. We have previously shown (Lance and Taub 1969; Zatz and Lance 1970) that lymph node localization directly reflects the recirculating lymphoid subpopulation while the splenic localization is composed of a recirculating cell component equal in numbers to that homing to the lymph nodes and an additional component of cells which preferentially localize in the spleen. Therefore, for clarity of presentation the percentage and number of cells localizing in recipient lymph nodes will be called the recirculating population while the non-recirculating population will refer to those cells localizing in the spleen after the recirculating component has been subtracted.

Antilymphocyte serum

As we have shown (Taub and Lance 1968), the administration of even small single doses of ALS leads to a swift, drastic and selective fall in the numbers of recirculating lymphoid cells (Table II). The proportion of non-recirculating cells is ordinarily unaffected or even slightly increased. Recovery proceeds slowly and gradually (Table III, Fig. 1), taking about fifty days before the normal range is re-entered. There is an acute rise in the amount of label localizing in the liver, which subsides over a few weeks.

Cortisol

The acute administration of small doses of cortisol caused a mild and transitory fall in the total cell yield from the lymph nodes of treated animals while the proportional distribution to recipient lymph node and spleen was unaffected, indicating that cortisol *per se* does not discriminate between lymphoid populations (Table IV). On the other hand, the chronic administration of 0·3 mg cortisol every three days led to a progressive decline in both varieties of lymphocyte subpopulations (Table V, Fig. 2).

The effect of cortisol on peripheral lymphocytes (lymph node cells) and central lymphocytes (thymocytes) is contrasted in Fig. 3. Groups of mice received two injections of cortisol two days apart and three days later the thymus and lymph nodes were removed, labelled and injected into panels of syngeneic recipients. A total dose of 0·5 mg of cortisol did not affect the numbers or distributions of lymph node cells, but higher doses caused a

TABLE IV

EFFECT OF CORTISOL TREATMENT ON THE DISTRIBUTION OF LYMPH NODE CELLS

Treatment	Percentage distribution				Number of cells migrating per donor mouse × 10^6				Total yield per donor mouse × 10^6
	Re-circulating population		Non-re-circulating population		Re-circulating population		Non-re-circulating population		
	Spleen population	Liver	Spleen population	Liver	Spleen population	Liver	Spleen population	Liver	
Normal mice	13·1 ±2·2	23·0 ±0·5	9·9	13·4 ±0·3	6·5	11·6	5·1	6·7	50
Three injections of cortisol, 0·1 mg/day per mouse	14·7 ±0·7	21·3 ±2·1	6·6	14·6 ±1·4	7·8	11·3	3·5	7·7	53
Three injections of cortisol, 0·2 mg/day per mouse	14·9 ±1·8	20·6 ±0·8	5·7	13·2 ±1·0	4·9	6·8	1·9	4·3	33

Cortisol injected on 3 consecutive days with migration 7 days after the last injection.

TABLE V

EFFECT OF CONTINUOUS CORTISOL TREATMENT

Cortisol given twice weekly, 0.3 mg.

			Day				Control
		+2	+6	+9	+12	+16	
Cell yield per donor mouse ×10^6	Recirculating	15	15	11	10	2.4	25
		12.9 ±0.5	13.8 ±0.9	12.4 ±1.1	11.2 ±2.0	4.5 ±0.3	12.8 ±2.2
Percentage distribution	Spleen	18.4 ±0.4	21.7 ±1.7	25.2 ±0.5	19.2 ±0.3	9.0 ±0.4	21.4 ±1.9
	Non-recirculating	5.5	7.9	12.8	8.0	4.5	8.6
	Liver	12.3 ±0.9	12.6 ±0.2	12.4 ±0.4	11.0 ±0.6	9.0 ±1.0	11.3 ±0.7
Numbers of cells ×10^6 migrating per donor mouse	Recirculating	1.42	1.52	1.07	0.84	0.11	3.5
	Spleen	2.02	2.38	2.2	1.4	0.24	5.9
	Non-recirculating	0.60	0.86	1.13	0.56	0.13	2.3
	Liver	1.35	1.38	1.06	0.83	0.24	3.2

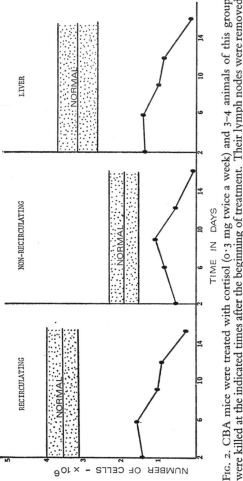

Fig. 2. CBA mice were treated with cortisol (0·3 mg twice a week) and 3–4 animals of this group were killed at the indicated times after the beginning of treatment. Their lymph nodes were removed and used for the migration assay.

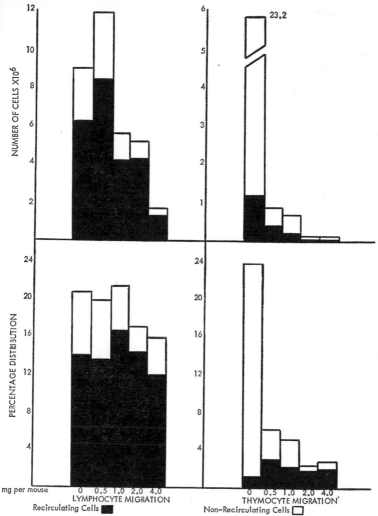

FIG. 3. The effect of increasing doses of cortisol on the percentages and numbers of cells belonging to recirculating and non-recirculating subpopulations of recipient lymph node and thymus. Migration was assayed three days after cortisol treatment. See text for details.

progressive and proportional decline in both recirculating and non-recirculating components. Thymocytes were more sensitive to cortisol than lymph node cells, since 0·5 mg (a dose not affecting lymph node cells) caused a drastic fall in cell numbers while higher doses virtually ablated the yield of thymic cells. Moreover, in contrast to the effect on peripheral cells, a differential effect on thymocytes was found: recirculating thymocytes were less affected at lower doses than non-recirculating cells. This suggests that immature thymocytes are more susceptible to the action of cortisol than thymocytes which have already acquired the property of recirculation.

The effect of cortisol on lymph node lymphocytes *in vitro* was determined in a number of separate experiments. Exposure to cortisol at concentrations of 2 mg/ml for four hours caused a drastic reduction in the migration of these cells to lymphoid compartments after injection into syngeneic recipients. On the other hand, the distribution was unaltered after incubation with lower concentrations of cortisol (0·2 mg/ml) or after relatively brief incubations (30–40 minutes).

The combination of ALS and cortisol

The remarkable ability of cortisol to maintain a state of immuno-suppression induced by ALS was documented in part I of this study. In a simulation of this protocol, two groups of mice were treated with 1·5 ml total dosage of ALS, after which one group received no further treatment while the other received injections of 0·5 mg of cortisol twice a week thereafter. The results are shown in Fig. 4. The recovery of recirculating lymphocytes in cortisol-treated animals was considerably retarded and, furthermore, a reduction in non-recirculating cells was found. This pattern conforms well to predictions based on summation of the curve obtained for ALS treatment alone and that found for chronic treatment with cortisol.

When ALS treatment is preceded by acute treatment with small doses of cortisol, the major alteration in population dynamics is a lag in the recovery of recirculating lymphocytes (Fig. 5). In this experiment two groups of animals received 1·0 ml of antilymphocyte serum either without pretreatment or preceded by three daily injections of 0·1 mg of cortisol (a dosage without effect on lymph node lymphocytes). The amount of depression

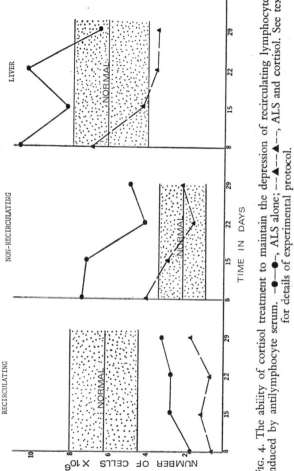

FIG. 4. The ability of cortisol treatment to maintain the depression of recirculating lymphocytes induced by antilymphocyte serum. —●—, ALS alone; --▲--, ALS and cortisol. See text for details of experimental protocol.

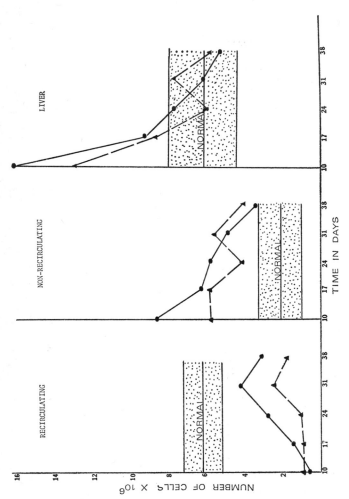

FIG. 5. One of two ALS-treated groups of mice was pretreated with a three-day course of cortisol (total dose 0·3 mg). A lag in the recovery of recirculating lymph node lymphocytes was found which extended over a three-week period. —●—, ALS alone; --▲--, ALS and cortisol.

TABLE VI

RECOVERY OF ADRENALECTOMIZED MICE FROM ALS TREATMENT

	ALS-treated adrenalectomized mice					ALS-treated sham-adrenalectomized mice				
Day:	+4	+17	+31	+45	+73	+4	+17	+31	+45	+73
Cell yield per donor mouse × 10⁶	30	29	41	49	53	23	38	19	26	32
Percentage distribution										
Recirculating population — Spleen	3·3 ±0·3	7·5 ±0·2	12·1 ±0·6	10·2 ±0·6	11·7 ±1·3	3·5 ±0·1	8·7 ±0·4	9·3 ±0·3	14·4 ±2·0	11·9 ±1·2
Spleen	15·6 ±0·6	20·5 ±1·2	17·7 ±0·8	20·5 ±0·6	23·5 ±1·9	15·8 ±1·7	20·1 ±0·4	16·3 ±1·3	19·7 ±1·1	21·8 ±1·4
Non-recirculating population — Liver	12·3	13·0	5·6	10·3	11·8	12·3	11·4	7·0	5·3	9·9
Liver	26·9 ±2·8	17·3 ±1·1	20·4 ±1·1	15·1 ±0·8	13·4 ±0·7	26·9 ±1·0	16·2 ±0·9	24·2 ±0·9	14·1 ±1·7	12·9 ±0·5
Number of cells migrating per donor mouse × 10⁶										
Recirculating population — Spleen	1·0	2·2	5·0	5·0	6·2	1·0	3·3	1·8	3·7	3·8
Spleen	4·7	6·0	7·3	10·0	12·0	3·6	7·6	3·2	4·2	7·0
Non-recirculating population — Liver	3·7	3·8	2·3	5·0	5·8	2·6	4·3	1·4	0·5	3·2
Liver	8·1	5·0	8·4	7·4	7·1	6·2	6·2	4·6	3·7	4·2

Adrenalectomy or sham operation were performed 3 days before the injection of 1·0 ml of ALS. Migration of lymph node cells from treated animals was assessed at the indicated intervals after treatment.

of the recirculating component in lymph nodes was initially identical. However, animals treated with ALS alone showed a progressive climb towards normal whereas in those in which ALS was preceded by cortisol, there was a lag period of three weeks before recovery started. In this protocol no differences were found for non-recirculating subpopulations.

Adrenalectomy

Adrenalectomy alone produced no changes in either cell yield or distributional properties of CBA lymph node or thymocyte populations. However, adrenalectomized mice receiving antilymphocytic serum had a more rapid recovery in the numbers of recirculating lymphocytes than those which had been sham operated. The results of a typical experiment are shown in Table VI where both groups of animals received a total dose of $1 \cdot 0$ ml of antilymphocyte serum. Adrenalectomy or sham operation was performed three days prior to ALS treatment.

Thymectomy

Animals thymectomized as neonates or as adults in conjunction with lethal irradiation plus bone marrow reconstitution were found to have a selective and marked decrease in recirculating lymphocytes (Table VII). Animals thymectomized as adults, but without any additional treatment, showed no change in the distributional characteristics of lymph node cells over a two-month period of observation.

The combination of adult thymectomy, cortisol and ALS

The results of an experiment designed to test the effects on lymph node populations of using thymectomy, ALS and cortisol in various combinations are illustrated in Tables VIII and IX. Groups of adult mice were thymectomized two weeks before the administration of either $0 \cdot 6$ mg of cortisol, $0 \cdot 6$ ml of ALS or the two agents together. An additional group of normal mice received both ALS and cortisol. The lymph nodes of these animals were removed 8, 14 and 21 days after cessation of treatment and used in the migration assay. The combination of adult thymectomy and this dose of cortisol did not produce any significant change in the composition of lymph node tissue, as the values were within the range of normal. Thymectomized

TABLE VII

EFFECT OF THYMECTOMY ON THE DISTRIBUTION OF LYMPH NODE LYMPHOCYTES

| | Percentage distribution | | |
	Lymph nodes	Spleen	Liver
Normal controls	15·3 ±1·2	19·8 ±0·4	14·9 ±1·2
Adult thymectomy (migration at 2 months)	14·6 ±2·9	22·7 ±1·3	13·0 ±0·8
Neonatal thymectomy (migration at 1 month)	2·8 ±1·0	19·4 ±0·3	32·1 ±1·8
Adult thymectomy (at 8 weeks; 900 R at 4 months; migration at 8 months)	1·8 ±0·5	18·2 ±1·6	28·1 ±1·3

TABLE VIII

EFFECT OF THYMECTOMY, ALS AND CORTISOL

Percentage distribution

Day:	Recirculating population			Spleen			Non-recirculating population			Liver		
	+8	+14	+21	+8	+14	+21	+8	+14	+21	+8	+14	+21
Thymectomized mice treated with hydrocortisone acetate	14·9 ±1·8	10·7 ±1·2	12·0 ±1·6	20·6 ±0·8	17·8 ±2·5	23·8 ±2·6	5·7	7·1	11·8	13·2 ±1·0	15·1 ±0·7	13·5 ±0·9
Thymectomized mice treated with ALS	2·5 ±1·2	2·9 ±0·2	3·6 ±0·9	16·5 ±0·6	15·1 ±2·6	20·6 ±0·7	14·0	12·2	17·0	27·2 ±2·4	22·1 ±0·9	20·8 ±0·9
Thymectomized mice treated with ALS and hydrocortisone acetate	3·1 ±0·6	3·5 ±0·9	3·2 ±0·3	16·2 ±1·3	14·5 ±0·3	21·2 ±1·5	13·1	11·0	18·0	22·4 ±3·2	23·7 ±1·2	19·7 ±1·0
Normal mice treated with ALS and hydrocortisone acetate	3·0 ±0·9	3·0 ±0·4	3·4 ±0·2	14·9 ±0·8	15·3 ±1·5	21·6 ±1·2	11·9	12·3	18·2	26·6 ±4·6	21·9 ±2·6	18·7 ±0·3

See text for details of experimental protocol.

TABLE IX

EFFECT OF THYMECTOMY, ALS AND CORTISOL

Number of cells migrating per donor mouse × 10^6

Day:	Recirculating population			Spleen			Non-recirculating population			Liver		
	+8	+14	+21	+8	+14	+21	+8	+14	+21	+8	+14	+21
Thymectomized mice treated with hydrocortisone acetate	4·9	3·9	8·5	6·8	6·4	16·8	1·9	2·5	8·3	4·3	5·4	9·5
Thymectomized mice treated with ALS	1·1	0·9	1·3	6·9	4·7	7·7	5·8	3·8	6·4	11·5	6·9	7·8
Thymectomized mice treated with ALS and hydrocortisone acetate	1·1	0·9	1·4	5·3	4·1	9·1	4·2	3·2	7·7	7·4	6·6	8·5
Normal mice treated with ALS and hydrocortisone acetate	0·8	0·8	1·6	4·2	3·8	9·9	3·4	3·0	8·3	7·5	5·5	8·6

See text for details of experimental protocol.

mice treated with antilymphocyte serum showed a marked depression of recirculating lymphocytes throughout the period of observation.* The combination of thymectomy, ALS and cortisol produced changes which were both qualitatively and quantitatively identical to those of the preceding group. Moreover, normal mice treated with ALS and cortisol displayed a similar range of effects. In this assay system, therefore, thymectomy or cortisol were interchangeable agents in their effects on ALS-treated animals and the combination of the two was not additive.

DISCUSSION

In part I of this study, the remarkable functional synergism between antilymphocyte serum and cortisol on the prolongation of skin allografts in mice was documented. In this second part, studies were made to elucidate the underlying changes in lymphoid populations to help explain this functional synergism and the mode of action of the agents themselves. A position of pre-eminence has been assigned to thymus-derived recirculating lymphocytes in the transaction of cell-mediated immunities (Gowans and McGregor 1965; Miller and Osoba 1967). Antilymphocyte serum is believed to achieve its potent immunosuppressive effects primarily through deletion of this population of cells (Lance 1968, 1969, 1970). The assay model used in these studies has previously been used to quantify this effect (Taub and Lance 1968).

The synergism between antilymphocyte serum and thymectomy has been previously described by Monaco, Wood and Russell (1965), while Levey and Medawar (1966b) have described the functional interaction between ALS and the adrenal axis. Our studies have shown that thymectomy considerably retards the recovery of the recirculating lymphocyte pool in animals treated with ALS. If a threshold number of these cells is required for allograft rejection, then the augmentation of immunosuppression under these circumstances is readily explained.

Cortisol appears to affect lymphoid populations in two distinct

* In other unpublished experiments thymectomized ALS-treated animals were followed over several months. Marked retardation in the recovery of the recirculating lymph node component was noted and these animals did not reach normal levels even after 120 days.

ways. In small doses a marked depletion of thymocytes occurs, simulating, therefore, a "chemical" thymectomy. At these low doses peripheral lymphoid tissue, as exemplified by the lymph node lymphocyte population, is not affected. The exquisite sensitivity of thymocytes to small doses of cortisol is not surprising and, indeed, has been used in the past as the basis for a bioassay of cortisol activity (Santísteban and Dougherty 1954). All thymocytes are not equally sensitive to the action of cortisol. In a previous study (Lance and Taub 1969) we showed that a small proportion of thymocytes *in situ* (about 5 per cent) possessed the property of recirculating. Presumably, this subpopulation represents the more mature members of the thymic population. Cortisol appears to discriminate in favour of this mature subcomponent and has a much more deleterious action upon immature thymocytes. In this respect, the findings of Blomgren and Andersson (1969) are of interest. They reported that cortisol-resistant thymic cells were ten times more reactive than the whole thymocyte population when measured in a graft-versus-host test system, suggesting that treatment with cortisol enriches the thymic population with cells at the mature, immunologically competent, end of the scale.

With these findings in mind, the functional mimicry between combinations of antilymphocyte serum and small doses of cortisol and of antilymphocyte serum and thymectomy is not surprising, nor is it difficult to understand why the combined administration of cortisol and thymectomy to ALS-treated recipients was no more effective than either agent alone.

In larger doses cortisol has an augmented effect upon the thymus and a direct lympholytic action on peripheral lymphoid tissues. With respect to peripheral lymphoid tissues, cortisol does not discriminate between recirculating and non-recirculating lymphoid populations.

Adrenalectomy was found to curtail the immunosuppressive effect of antilymphocyte serum, and the kinetic studies of lymphoid populations provide a tentative explanation in terms of a more rapid regeneration of recirculating lymphocytes.

The question of whether treatment with cortisol induces qualitative changes in lymphoid populations as well as quantitative changes is not answerable on the basis of these studies. Nonetheless, the functional synergism observed in the skin allograft studies can be understood by the additive effects of these various agents on lymphoid subpopulations.

SUMMARY (PARTS I AND II)

The functional interrelationship between antilymphocyte serum, manipulations of the adrenal axis and/or thymectomy were studied in a murine model of skin allotransplantation. The accompanying changes in lymphoid cell populations were documented using a model of lymphocyte migration which allows us to measure the proportional representation of lymphoid subpopulations. The immunosuppressive effects of these agents can be understood in terms of the changes they induce in the relevant subpopulations of lymphoid cells.

Acknowledgements

The work described in part II was supported by graduate training grant TI-AM-5414 of The National Institute for Arthritis and Metabolism, U.S.P.H.S. and by P.H.S. grant AI-08750 of the National Institute of Allergy and Infectious Diseases, National Institutes of Health.

REFERENCES

ADDISON, T. (1855) *On the Constitutional and Local Effects of Diseases of the Supra-Renal Capsules.* London: Highley.

BILLINGHAM, R. E., KROHN, P. L. and MEDAWAR, P. B. (1951a) *Br. med. J.* **1**, 1157–1163.

BILLINGHAM, R. E., KROHN, P. L. and MEDAWAR, P. B. (1951b) *Br. med. J.* **2**, 1049–1053.

BLOMGREN, H. and ANDERSSON, B. (1969) *Expl Cell Res.* **57**, 185.

DOUGHERTY, T. F. (1952) *Physiol Rev.* **32**, 379.

DOUGHERTY, T. F. (1960) In *The Lymphocyte and Lymphocytic Tissue*, p. 112, ed. Rebuck, J. W. New York: Hoeber.

GOWANS, J. L. and McGREGOR, D. D. (1965) *Prog. Allergy* **9**, 1.

KROHN, P. L. (1954) *J. Endocr.* **11**, 78.

LANCE, E. M. (1968) In *Advances in Transplantation* (Proc. I Int. Congr. Transplantation Society), p. 107, ed. Dausset, J., Hamburger, J. and Mathé, G. Copenhagen: Munksgaard.

LANCE, E. M. (1969) *J. exp. Med.* **130**, 49.

LANCE, E. M. (1970) *Fedn Proc. Fedn Am. Socs exp. Biol.* **29**, 209–211.

LANCE, E. M. and MEDAWAR, P. B. (1969) *Proc. R. Soc. B* **173**, 447.

LANCE, E. M. and TAUB, R. N. (1969) *Nature, Lond.* **221**, 841.

LEVEY, R. H. and MEDAWAR, P. B. (1966a) *Ann. N.Y. Acad. Sci.* **129**, 164.

LEVEY, R. H. and MEDAWAR, P. B. (1966b) *Proc. natn. Acad. Sci. U.S.A.* **56**, 1130.

MEDAWAR, P. B. (1968) In *Human Transplantation*, p. 501, ed. Rapaport, F. T. and Dausset, J. New York: Grune & Stratton.
MEDAWAR, P. B. and SPARROW, E. M. (1956) *J. Endocr.* **14**, 240.
MILLER, J. F. A. P. and OSOBA, D. (1967) *Physiol Rev.* **47**, 437.
MONACO, A. P., WOOD, M. L. and RUSSELL, P. S. (1965) *Science* **149**, 432.
SANTÍSTEBAN, G. A. and DOUGHERTY, T. F. (1954) *Endocrinology* **54**, 130.
SELYE, H. (1946) *J. clin. Endocr. Metab.* **6**, 117.
TAUB, R. N. and LANCE, E. M. (1968) *Immunology* **15**, 633.
ZATZ, M. M. and LANCE, E. M. (1970) *Cell Immun.* **1**, 1.

DISCUSSION

Humphrey: What are the cells which do not recirculate and which you therefore don't see in lymph nodes?

Lance: The non-recirculating (spleen-seeking population) has not been completely characterized yet. We do know that short-lived lymphocytes, macrophages and haematopoietic elements preferentially migrate to the spleen but I am sure that doesn't account for more than a fraction of the non-recirculating population. Our guess at the moment is that the non-recirculating component found in the normal lymph node tissue consists of those cells anatomically located in the cortex, germinal centres and medullary areas.

A. White: You described incubating thymocytes *in vitro* with hydrocortisone; have you tried incubating the cells with steroids such as progesterone? In our experience, progesterone added *in vitro* in concentrations of 10^{-4}M to rat thymocytes will lead to death of the cells.

Lance: We haven't tried other steroids yet.

A. White: In the experiments in which you prolonged allograft retention by administering hydrocortisone and then ALS, were you able to achieve the same prolongation by giving additional ALS alone?

Lance: Yes. In the allograft model, hydrocortisone and antilymphocyte serum were interchangeable agents in maintaining a state of immunosuppression originally induced by treatment with antilymphocyte serum.

A. White: Dr J. N. Esteban (1968) has reported that an injection of hydrocortisone rather specifically destroys the short-lived rather than the long-lived lymphocytes. Perhaps, therefore, if you gave a dose of hydrocortisone first, your ALS would have fewer cells remaining and a given dose of ALS would, in a manner of speaking, be available to attack a greater number of the remaining immunologically competent cells.

Lance: The synergistic effects of ALS and cortisone probably depend to a large extent on dosage and timing. At the low dose levels of hydrocortisone ($0 \cdot 1$ mg $\times 3$) used in the potentiation experiments, we were unable to demonstrate an effect on peripheral lymphoid tissues. However, at this same dose, we found a drastic effect on the population of thymocytes. We feel, therefore, that at low doses, hydrocortisone acts to vitiate the thymic contribution to the recovery of recirculating lymphocytes and, therefore, prolongs the state of immunosuppression induced by a given dose of antilymphocyte serum. In the maintenance experiments repeated small doses of steroids were given for an indefinite period of time and in this case the state of immunosuppression induced by antilymphocyte serum was prolonged over the duration of steroid treatment. We feel this thymic action mimics the effect of thymectomy, and indeed our data which directly compared the effects of small doses of steroids and thymectomy bear out this contention.

At higher doses hydrocortisone has a direct lytic effect on peripheral lymphoid cells as well as an action through the thymus. Treatment with high doses of steroids would then be expected to have an ALS-sparing effect.

We tend to think of skin graft rejection in terms of requiring a threshold number of recirculating lymphoid cells. According to this view, any treatment or combination of treatments which reduces the numbers of recirculating lymphocytes below this threshold will thwart skin allograft rejection and any treatment or combination of treatments which prevents regeneration of recirculating lymphocytes will maintain this state of immunosuppression and prevent skin allograft rejection. What is so dramatic is the functional synergism between antilymphocyte serum and very small doses of steroids of the hydrocortisone type exhibited in a species generally thought of as rather insensitive to steroid treatment.

Owen: Schlesinger and Golakai (1967) have shown that hydrocortisone depletes TL-positive cells of the mouse thymus and that it takes some time for these cells to reappear. How would this fit in with your observations?

Lance: We have studied the question of the TL antigen in the maturation of mouse thymocytes (Lance *et al.* 1970). We find that a small percentage of thymocytes *in situ* are TL-negative and it is this small TL-negative population which has also acquired the property of recirculation. We can recover this TL-negative population of thymocytes by taking advantage of their ability to localize in lymph nodes, and we have tested their immuno-competence in a graft-versus-host system. It turns out that this subpopulation of thymocytes are just about as efficient, cell for cell, as lymph node lymphocytes in producing splenomegaly in suitable F_1 hybrids. Moreover, Leckband (1970) has shown that treatment of thymocytes *in vitro* with antisera directed towards the TL antigen leaves behind a residue of TL-negative thymocytes which are highly efficient in graft-versus-host reactions. This fits in very nicely with the data we have presented, because hydrocortisone in the doses we were using selectively removed the immature, non-recirculating thymocytes—that is, the TL-positive ones.

King: Do you know whether the ability of ALS to potentiate the effect of cortisol is a specific or non-specific effect of ALS? I ask this because serum, and possibly some tissues, contain a protein that binds cortisol and in so doing lowers the biological activity of cortisol. If you are making an antibody to that binding protein in the course of making your antilymphocyte serum, you will possibly potentiate the effect of cortisol just by taking out the binding protein itself.

Lance: We have not considered that possibility, but do not feel it is necessary to postulate an additional mechanism to explain our findings, since the synergism between ALS and hydro-cortisone can be explained by the direct additive effects of their individual actions on lymphoid populations.

King: I would put it the other way round: can you rule it out?

Lance: No, we can't exclude it.

A. White: Dr Quint, Dr Hardy and Dr Monaco have studied the effects of ALS on allograft survival in mice (Hardy, Quint and Monaco 1970). Skin grafts from C3H mice were placed upon A/He mice. The normal mean survival time of the skin graft was 10 days. These investigations confirmed our previous report (Hardy *et al.* 1968) that one can accelerate allograft rejection, that is, increase host-cell-mediated immunological competence, by preceding the grafting with 7 daily injections of 4 mg of thymosin protein. Hardy, Quint and Monaco have now (1970) reported that administration of an anti-mouse lymphocyte serum (ALS) prepared in rabbits for 7 days before grafting results in prolongation (~25 days) of the skin grafts. This is the well established immunosuppressive effect of ALS. Most surprising was the observation that if thymosin was administered 6 hours before ALS for 7 days before skin grafting, there was a remarkable prolongation of the skin graft (~52 days), significantly beyond that obtained with ALS alone. Administration of thymosin and normal rabbit serum together resulted in a mean survival time of the allograft similar to that seen with thymosin alone (~8 days). If bovine serum albumin is given as a control in place of thymosin 6 hours before ALS, allograft survival time is approximately that obtained with ALS alone. The data indicate therefore that if thymosin is administered before allografting, rejection of the allograft is accelerated. In contrast, if thymosin is injected shortly before ALS, there is a marked prolongation of the survival of the skin graft beyond that seen with ALS alone. The conclusion appears warranted that, depending on the dose schedule, one can with thymosin either potentiate or negate the effects of ALS. The general working hypothesis that Quint, Hardy and Monaco have put forward is that by giving thymosin 6 hours before ALS, you "flush" out the immunologically competent cells which are then more readily hit by the ALS.

Humphrey: If you give pertussis vaccine in the morning and ALS in the afternoon, you also potentiate the effect of ALS. Have you actually demonstrated by cell counts that thymosin will flush out thymus cells?

Goldstein: Drs Hardy, Quint and Monaco (1970) have examined the histology of the lymph nodes of mice treated with thymosin and ALS. They found a marked depletion in the so-called thymus-dependent areas, which was more extensive after the combined treatment with thymosin and ALS than after ALS alone.

Lance: Do their results suggest that thymosin may work like pertussis vaccine, being an adjuvant potentiating the response of animals?

Goldstein: Pertussis is a very complex antigen whose modes of action have not yet been explained. I might add that Drs Hardy, Quint and Monaco (personal communication) have found that they could *not* achieve with pertussis the marked prolongation of allograft survival (> 52 days) seen in mice given thymosin 6 hours before ALS.

REFERENCES

ESTEBAN, J. N. (1968) *Anat. Rec.* **162,** 349.

HARDY, M. A., QUINT, J., GOLDSTEIN, A. L., STATE, D. and WHITE, A. (1968) *Proc. natn. Acad. Sci. U.S.A.* **61,** 875.

HARDY, M. A., QUINT, J. and MONACO, A. P. (1970) *J. Reticuloendothelial Soc.* **7,** 656.

LANCE, E. M., COOPER, S., BUCHHAGEN, D. and BOYSE, E. A. (1970) *Fedn Proc. Fedn Am. Socs exp. Biol.* **29**(2), 436 (abst. 1073).

LECKBAND, E. (1970) *Fedn Proc. Fedn Am. Socs exp. Biol.* **29**(2), 621 (abst. 2108).

SCHLESINGER, M. and GOLAKAI, V. K. (1967) *Science* **155,** 1114.

THE ESSENTIAL ROLE OF CORTICOSTEROIDS IN THE INDUCTION OF THE IMMUNE RESPONSE *IN VITRO*

C. T. AMBROSE

Department of Bacteriology and Immunology, Harvard Medical School, Boston, Massachusetts

NUMEROUS studies have demonstrated that adrenocortical hormones produce lymphocytolysis (Hechter and Johnson 1949), thymic involution (Santísteban and Dougherty 1954), and inhibition of antibody synthesis (Mirick 1951; Fagraeus 1952). These effects provide a rational basis for the clinical use of corticosteroids in the treatment of allergic diseases and during transplantation surgery. Thus the prevalent assumption is that corticosteroids depress the immune response, or exert a negative influence on the immune system. It is, therefore, somewhat heretical to advance the view that the immune response is absolutely dependent on corticosteroids for its induction. But this is the first of two theses I wish to propose here and is based on our studies with steroids in an antibody-producing organ culture system. The second thesis concerns the so-called permissive action of steroids and proposes that certain corticosteroids "facilitate" derepression of genes by unmasking sites on the DNA of chromatin for attachment of natural signals or inducers. This proposal is based on our studies measuring the binding of actinomycin D to DNA and to chromatin in the presence and absence of cortisol (hydrocortisone). These two theses provide an outline of this review of our work and necessitate two introductions—the first for the organ culture system and the second for the binding studies. The evolution of ideas leading from one to the other will, I hope, smooth the transition from the cellular to the subcellular level in this paper.

ANTIBODY PRODUCTION *IN VITRO*

Briefly, the organ culture system is that originated by Michaelides and Coons (1963) with some later modifications (Ambrose

1969). It involves measuring the secondary antibody response over the course of several weeks or months in organ cultures of rabbit lymph node fragments. Rabbits are primed with any of various antigens (tetanus or diphtheria toxoids, bovine serum albumin, etc.). Several months later, when the primary response has declined, the lymph nodes are excised, cut into fragments of 1 mm³ and incubated for several hours with the priming antigen(s) to elicit *in vitro* the secondary response. These stimulated fragments are then rinsed free of excess antigen and distributed among Leighton tubes. The fragments are held in place by an overlying pad of glass wool, which when moistened with medium clings to the inner side of the tube. A well-primed rabbit yields sufficient lymphoid tissue to prepare 25–100 culture tubes, depending on the number of fragments added to each tube. Four tubes or more are grouped together to test each variable in an experiment; their average response provides the data recorded here. One ml of culture medium added to each tube is replaced every three days over a three-week period in most experiments. These medium changes are saved for later assay of their antibody content by the haemagglutination method.

The major merit of this culture is that it makes available for study *in vitro* both the inductive and productive phases of the secondary response. The inductive phase, covering days 0–9 in this culture system, entails antigen stimulation, cell division, cell differentiation, and an exponential increase in antibody synthesis. The productive phase, which follows, shows little lymphoid cell division but yields high antibody production at a linear rate, often for more than a week before the secondary response begins to decline.

The medium originally used with these organ cultures consisted of 25 per cent rabbit serum in Eagle's medium. The latter contains salts, glucose and the so-called essential amino acids and vitamins. We observed that the secondary response is not supported *in vitro* by Eagle's medium alone nor by Eagle's medium supplemented with dialysed serum. However, Eagle's medium plus a dialysate of serum is effective. We determined that several dialysable components of serum (e.g. serine, vitamin B_{12} and insulin) may improve the response in Eagle's medium, but that cortisol is absolutely required (Ambrose 1964). Fig. 1 illustrates this basic observation, which led to the work presented

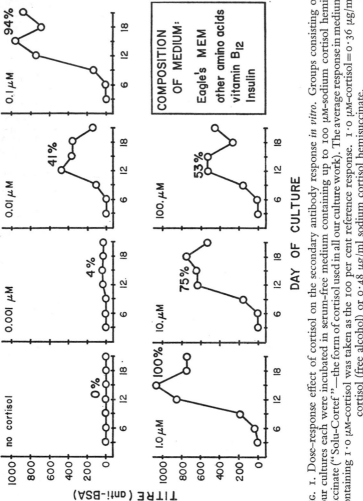

FIG. 1. Dose-response effect of cortisol on the secondary antibody response *in vitro*. Groups consisting of four cultures each were incubated in serum-free medium containing up to 100 μM-sodium cortisol hemisuccinate ("Solu-Cortef"—the form of cortisol used in all our culture work). The average response in medium containing 1·0 μM-cortisol was taken as the 100 per cent reference response. 1·0 μM-cortisol = 0·36 μg/ml cortisol (free alcohol) or 0·48 μg/ml sodium cortisol hemisuccinate.

here. The serum-free medium described in this figure failed to support the secondary response until it included cortisol at a concentration above 0·001 μM. The maximal response occurred in medium containing 0·1–1·0 μM cortisol. Higher levels proved progressively inhibitory. In rabbits the major adrenocortical steroid is not cortisol but corticosterone. Corticosterone proved equally effective in supporting the secondary response in these organ cultures; the optimal concentration of corticosterone was around 0·1 μM, which is within the range of the normal corticosterone concentration in rabbit serum (van der Vies 1961).

A large number of steroids were tested in this culture system for their capacity to support the immune response. None of the common progesterone derivatives, androgens or oestrogens could duplicate cortisol's supportive effect. And only certain corticosteroids proved active. These included cortisone and 11-dehydrocorticosterone, which are reduced to cortisol and corticosterone, respectively, in many cell cultures (Berliner and Dougherty 1961). Also active were cortexolone, 21-deoxycortisol, aldosterone, and various esters of cortisol as well as numerous synthetic derivatives, such as 9α-fluorocortisol and 16α-hydroxycortisol. Corticosteroids inactive in this culture system included cortexone (DOC), 11-epicortisol, 20β-dihydrocortisone and tetrahydrocortisol. Some of these steroids are depicted in Fig. 2.

We found cortisol to be essential for the immune response only during the inductive phase, as Fig. 3 illustrates. In this experiment cortisol was included in the serum-free medium for the periods indicated by the bar across the top of each graph. Only 0·01 μM-cortisol was used so that the extracellular concentration would be reduced to a negligible one after rinsing the tubes on day 3, 6 or 9, when the steroid was omitted from the medium. The 100 per cent reference response was produced by those cultures incubated for 21 days in medium with cortisol. Cultures maintained in medium free of cortisol produced no antibody. Inclusion of cortisol in the medium for only the first 3, 6 or 9 days supported increasingly greater responses, while omission of cortisol until day 3, 6 or 9 impaired the response progressively. Thus physiological levels of cortisol are required for some metabolic event(s) occurring during the inductive phase of these cultures.

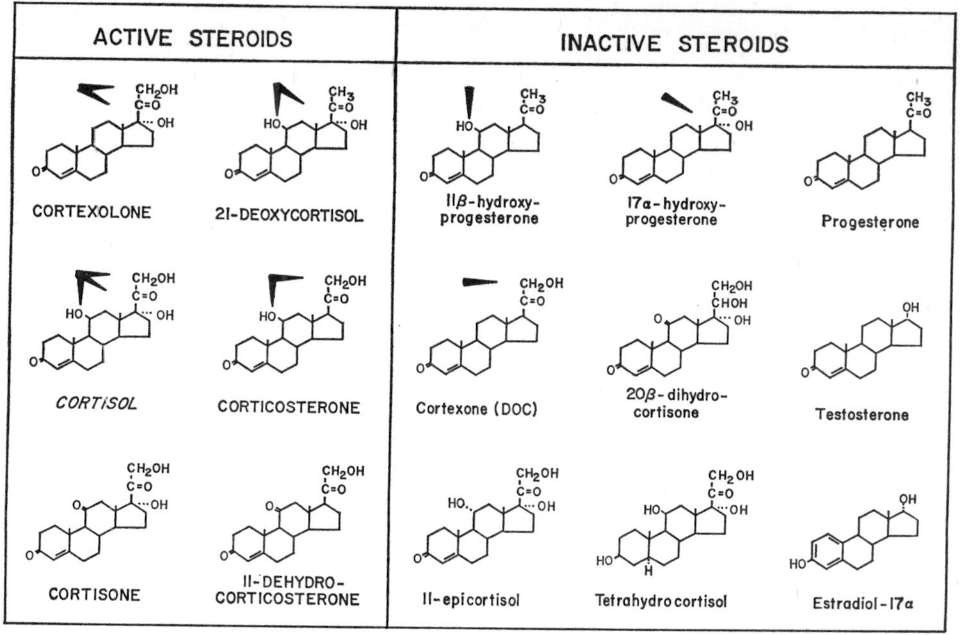

Fig. 2. The structural requirements for activity of corticoids which support the secondary response *in vitro*. The black arrows point up the importance of 11β-, 17α and 20-OH groups and show that any two of the three are sufficient and essential. The 11-oxo group is reduced to 11β-OH in this culture system.

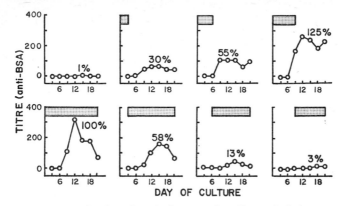

FIG. 3. Localization of cortisol's supportive effect to the inductive phase. The stippled bar above each graph indicates the period of treatment of cultures with serum-free medium containing 0·01 μM-cortisol. Each graph depicts the average response of four cultures treated alike.

In animals a requirement for cortisol during initiation of the immune response has not been clearly established. Various authors have reported different effects on the immune response after adrenalectomy (reviewed by Ambrose 1964). Their divergent results may reflect the difficulty of achieving complete adrenalectomy, since many animals possess unrecognized aberrant adrenal tissue (Fukuda 1952). This difficulty invalidates many such animal experiments and allows us to surmise that the requirement for cortisol *in vitro* probably exists also *in vivo*. This contention might be decided in animals surgically adrenalectomized and then treated with adrenocorticolytic drugs to render them also "chemically" adrenalectomized.

While examining other steroids for their ability to duplicate cortisol's supportive effect, we observed that 1·0 to 10 μM levels of progesterone, 17α-hydroxyprogesterone, testosterone, cis-testosterone, and both 17α- and 17β-oestradiol strongly inhibited the secondary response in the presence of 0·01 μM-cortisol. But little or no inhibition was produced by 10 μM levels of numerous other related steroids. Fig. 4 summarizes some of these data. An analysis of several dozen steroids so tested disclosed that a low polarity was the common physical prerequisite for inhibition.

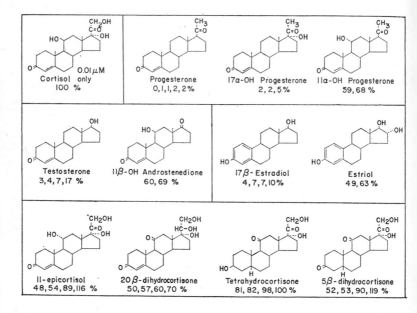

FIG. 4. The effect of 10 μM (10⁻⁵ M) levels of various steroids on the secondary response *in vitro* supported by 0·01 μM (10⁻⁸ M) cortisol. In the many experiments summarized here all media contained 0·01 μM-cortisol. In each experiment the control culture group which received no other steroid than 0·01 μM-cortisol provided the 100 per cent reference response for the other groups whose media contained also 10 μM of various other steroids. The percentage values listed thus reflect the inhibitory effect of the additional 10 μM steroid. Each experimental group contained four cultures.

For example, progesterone is very inhibitory, while the more polar 11α- and 11β-hydroxyprogesterone are not. Testosterone is very inhibitory, while less inhibitory are the more polar 11β-hydroxyandrostenedione, androsterone, dehydroepiandrosterone and etiocholanolone. Both oestradiols are strongly inhibitory, while the more polar oestriol is not. Of the many corticosteroids which fail to support the inductive phase, none inhibits antibody production at a concentration of 10 μM; again these inactive corticosteroids are all far more polar than any of the inhibitory steroids cited above.

This correlation between greater inhibition and low polarity pointed at first to a mechanism for inhibition by these steroids. Davidson, Devenuto and Westphal (1963) showed that the membranes and mitochondria of liver and kidney cells bind more avidly the less polar steroids, such as progesterone. The relatively high concentrations of these steroids needed to inhibit the immune response *in vitro* (1–10 μM) suggest a non-specific effect and possibly one concerned with coating the mitochondria or saturating various membranes and thus blocking normal metabolic exchange through them. However, an important feature of steroid inhibition in our lymph node cultures is that high levels of the non-polar steroids inhibit when added during the inductive phase but not when added only during the productive phase. This temporal difference is illustrated in Fig. 5 for testosterone.

An equally puzzling finding is that inhibition produced by these steroids is significantly reduced by increasing the concentration of cortisol in the medium from 0·01 μM to 1·0 μM. This reduction in inhibition is shown in Fig. 6 for progesterone. How cortisol, a highly polar molecule, provides this "protection" is not clear. It seems doubtful that the supportive role of cortisol (and certain other corticosteroids) and the inhibitory effect of progesterone (and other non-polar steroids) reside at the same cellular site.

These studies showing an interrelationship between the supportive corticoids and the inhibitory steroids were interesting but did not define their sites or modes of action. Consequently, we searched for some metabolic inhibitor whose mechanism is well defined and whose effect on antibody production *in vitro* is altered in some way by cortisol. We reasoned that such an action might result from a common site of action. From among a large

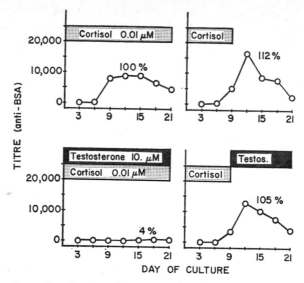

FIG. 5. Localization of testosterone's inhibitory effect to the inductive phase *in vitro*. The bars above each graph indicate the interval of treatment with 0·01 μM-cortisol and 10 μM-testosterone. There were four cultures in each experimental group. Testosterone added on day 9 produced no inhibitory effect (105 per cent compared to 112 per cent) but when included from day 0, it inhibited the response almost completely (4 per cent, compared to 100 per cent).

number of such inhibitors tested we found that only actinomycin D (AD) produced an effect altered by the presence of cortisol. Before discussing this interaction between cortisol and AD, let me describe two opposite effects of AD on antibody synthesis in this culture system.

Concentrations of AD greater than 0·01 μM stop antibody synthesis by preventing replenishment of messenger RNAs coding for heavy and light immunoglobulin chains and for other proteins vital to the culture's continued function. In contrast to this inhibition is a transient enhancement of antibody synthesis produced by a *short* exposure during the productive phase to *low* levels of AD (≤0·01 μM) (Ambrose 1969). We believe this enhancement is due to preferential inhibition by the AD pulse of

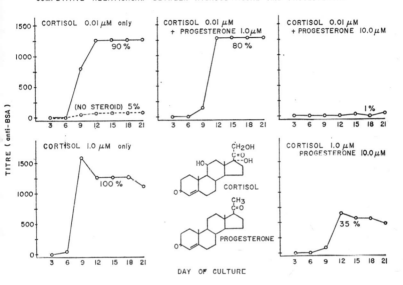

FIG. 6. The protective effect of a high concentration of cortisol on inhibition of the secondary response by progesterone. 10 μM-progesterone inhibited the response almost completely (1 per cent) in cultures supported by 0·01 μM-cortisol but reduced the response only to 35 per cent in cultures supported by 1·0 μM-cortisol. All percentage values refer to the 100 per cent reference response produced by the culture group supported by 1·0 μM-cortisol. The steroid concentrations cited were present in the medium of the cultures throughout their 21-day life. There were four cultures in each experimental group.

an inhibitory material usually produced by these cultures and normally regulating antibody synthesis during the productive phase. These opposite effects of high and low levels of AD were originally demonstrated during the productive phase in cultures whose medium contained 1·0 μM-cortisol. But you will recall that cortisol is not required during the productive phase and that an equally good response is produced when it is omitted from the medium after day 9. This feature of the culture system permitted us to test whether cortisol's presence during the productive phase influenced either the inhibition or the enhancement produced by high and low levels, respectively, of actinomycin. I will briefly summarize the results by saying that cortisol appears not only to hasten inhibition by high levels of AD but also to facilitate enhancement by low levels. These two entirely opposite effects of actinomycin are probably due to the same basic mechanism of preventing synthesis of mRNA, although different mRNAs are inhibited by the different levels of AD. Since this common mechanism entails binding of AD to guanine residues of DNA, we wondered whether cortisol might influence actinomycin's actions merely by facilitating its binding to DNA. We therefore sought some means of measuring directly the binding of AD to DNA in the presence and absence of cortisol.

BINDING OF ACTINOMYCIN D TO DNA AND TO CHROMATIN

I have referred to the fact that actinomycin binds specifically to the guanine residues of DNA (Reich and Goldberg 1964). Molecules of AD bound to DNA differ in several spectral parameters from unbound molecules free in solution. Such parameters include optical rotation and simple optical absorption at specific wavelengths. These spectral differences allow one to measure the binding capacity of DNA solutions by a simple titration scheme. For example, early in the titration of a DNA solution with AD, the optical rotation observed at 480 nm changes at a rate characteristic of actinomycin bound to DNA. But once all sites on the DNA are saturated with AD and as more AD is added, the optical rotation changes at a decreased rate characteristic now of actinomycin free in solution. A typical optical rotation titration is shown in Fig. 7. This titration was done in a Cary Model 60 Recording Spectropolarimeter at 480 nm. At this wavelength substantial optical rotation is produced only by AD and not by DNA or chromatin. The intersection of the two lines in this figure is a measure of the binding capacity of the DNA solution titrated. Ringertz and Bolund (1969) described a similar titration method utilizing the hypochromic and hyperchromic shifts which occur at 425 nm and 470 nm, respectively, for AD bound to DNA. We have used both titration methods to obtain the data and conclusions presented here.

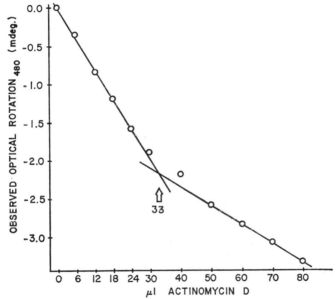

FIG. 7. A typical optical rotation titration of rabbit thymus DNA, demonstrating its relative binding capacity for actinomycin D. Three ml of a solution containing 80 µg isolated DNA was titrated with a solution containing 0·8 mg/ml of actinomycin D, added from a Hamilton repeating dispenser in 6 or 10 µl volumes. The titration was performed in a Cary Model 60 recording spectropolarimeter at 480 nm.

The binding data may be appraised more readily if I first summarize our major finding. Cortisol has little or no effect on the binding of AD to isolated DNA but increases, and often doubles, the binding of AD to isolated chromatin (Ambrose 1970). Chromatin consists of DNA surrounded by histones and other basic proteins and is the form in which DNA exists within the cell. Ringertz and Bolund (1969) showed that in different chromatin preparations AD binds only to 10–50 per cent of the potential sites on the underlying DNA. The other sites presumably are masked by the surrounding protein sheath. Our finding thus suggests that cortisol unmasks many of these occult binding sites for AD.

For these studies we isolated thymus chromatin from normal weanling male rabbits by the method of Bonner and co-workers (1968). DNA was isolated from this chromatin by centrifugation twice through 4 M-caesium chloride. The data presented in Table I were obtained from optical absorption titrations at 425 nm, according to the procedure devised by Ringertz and Bolund (1969). The first three experiments cited in Table I show that 50 μM-cortisol or corticosterone added to a cuvette containing a chromatin suspension resulted in a significant increase in binding, while equimolar amounts of two inactive corticosteroids (11-epicortisol and tetrahydrocortisol) produced no increase. In experiment 4 of Table I a chromatin preparation containing a total of 105 μg DNA showed an AD binding capacity of 41 μl. A similar binding capacity was demonstrated by an isolated DNA solution containing a total of only 19 μg DNA. Thus only about a fifth as much pure DNA was needed to bind the same quantity of AD as was bound by the chromatin preparation containing 105 μg DNA. This agrees well with the observation by Ringertz and Bolund mentioned above. The other significant feature of the data in experiment 4 is that 50 μM-cortisol added to the chromatin increased its binding capacity from 41 μl to 57 μl, while similar treatment of the DNA solution did not increase its binding capacity.

These observations are further supported in Table II, which records the data from optical rotation titrations. In experiments 1 and 2 a dose–response relationship is evident with the optimal concentration of cortisol being 50 μM; higher levels of cortisol appeared to reduce this increased binding capacity. The comparable enhancing effect of corticosterone is seen in experiment 3, while the absence of an effect from two physiologically inactive corticosteroids is shown in experiments 4 and 5. Finally

TABLE I

RELATIVE ACTINOMYCIN BINDING BY CHROMATIN AND DNA, BASED ON ABSORPTION TITRATIONS AT 425 NM

| | Experiment 1 | Experiment 2 | Experiment 3 | Experiment 4 | |
	Chromatin	Chromatin	Chromatin	Chromatin 105 μg DNA	Isolated DNA 19 μg DNA
No steroid (control)	33	42	27	41	34, 37, 39
50 μM-cortisol	44	72	52	57	33, 35, 36
50 μM-corticosterone	45				
50 μM-11-epicortisol		42			
50 μM-tetrahydrocortisol			29		

The alcohol form of the steroids was added in a methanol solution to a standard Zeiss spectrophotometer cuvette (1 cm path length) and evaporated to dryness before adding 3 ml of either a diluted chromatin suspension or a DNA solution. The volume of steroid solution used was sufficient to yield the desired concentration in the final 3 ml. Actinomycin D (0·8 mg/ml) was added in 2, 4 or 6 μl volumes from a Hamilton repeating dispenser and the reactants mixed with a glass stirring rod before the optical density was read at 425 nm. The binding values listed refer only to the volume of the actinomycin solution which saturated the tight binding sites on the chromatin or DNA in the cuvette. These values are a simple and direct means of comparing the relative binding capacity of replicate chromatin suspensions or DNA solutions under different conditions.

The four experiments used different chromatin preparations; this partly accounts for the different binding capacities obtained in the control titrations. The percentage increase in binding capacity produced by 50 μM-cortisol varied from 30 per cent in experiment 1 to 90 per cent in experiment 4. This variation is possibly due to the chromatin preparations having been sheared to different degrees; greater shearing would make a preparation more DNA-like in terms of its binding capacity. Similarly, old chromatin has an increased template activity; thus ageing is probably another variable affecting the binding response of chromatin to cortisol in these experiments.

TABLE II

RELATIVE ACTINOMYCIN BINDING BY CHROMATIN AND DNA, BASED ON OPTICAL ROTATION TITRATIONS

| | Chromatin | | | | | DNA |
| | Dose response | | Other corticoids | | | |
	Experiment 1	Experiment 2	Experiment 3	Experiment 4	Experiment 5	Experiment 6
No steroid	67, 78	48, 54	45, 58	66, 72	78, 84	20, 26
5 μM-cortisol	68					28
25 μM-cortisol	92, 104					
50 μM-cortisol	128, 130	118, 126	104, 134	108, 119	114, 116	26, 32
75 μM-cortisol	94, 98					
100 μM-cortisol		74				
50 μM-corticosterone			94			
50 μM-11-epicorticosterone				66		
50 μM-tetrahydrocortisol					78	

Essentially the same procedure was followed for these titrations as for the optical absorption titrations. See legends for Table I and Fig. 7.

experiment 6 demonstrates again that an isolated DNA preparation shows relatively little or no increased binding of AD upon treatment with 5 or 50 μM-cortisol.

A number of recent reports suggest that *some* primary effects of steroid hormones are produced at the level of transcription (reviewed by Tata 1966). For example, liver nuclei (Ohtsuka and Koide 1969) and liver chromatin (Stackhouse, Chetsanga and Tan 1968) prepared from adrenalectomized rats exhibit a given template activity *in vitro* which is significantly increased when cortisol is added to either subcellular system. Our explanation for the increased actinomycin-binding of cortisol-treated chromatin may equally well apply to this cortisol-augmented capacity of nuclei or chromatin to prime for RNA synthesis. Several authors have reported extensively on the binding of cortisol to histones (Sluyser 1969; Brunkhorst 1969). Our finding that cortisol increases the binding capacity of thymus chromatin but not of thymus DNA suggests that cortisol unmasks binding sites on the underlying DNA core by interacting with the protein of chromatin. If cortisol exposes such binding sites for actinomycin D, it may expose still other areas of the DNA of chromatin. Therefore, on the basis of our binding studies we propose that biologically active corticosteroids mediate their permissive effects in cells by unmasking sites on the DNA of chromatin for attachment of natural signals or inducers. Through this mechanism corticosteroids (and possibly steroids in general) may facilitate derepression in higher cells.

SUMMARY

The secondary antibody response can be initiated in lymph node organ cultures prepared from primed rabbits and the ensuing antibody synthesis followed in these cultures for many weeks. When serum-free medium is used, the inductive phase (day 0–9) exhibits an absolute requirement for physiological levels (0·01–0·1 μM) of cortisol, corticosterone, or certain related active corticosteroids. Other steroids (progesterone, testosterone, oestrogen) do not support the response and at 1–10 μM levels are inhibitory during the inductive phase. This inhibition is partially overcome by cortisol at high, non-toxic levels (1–10 μM). Synthesis of antibody during the productive phase (day 9 onward) is not influenced by any of the above steroids at concentrations of 10 μM or less.

Of the commonly used metabolic inhibitors with defined modes of action we found only actinomycin D (AD) to be influenced by cortisol in this culture system. Cortisol appears to enhance or facilitate AD's inhibition of protein synthesis. This interaction was studied further in a subcellular system employing rabbit thymus chromatin. The binding capacity of chromatin for AD is increased by cortisol or corticosterone but not by various other inactive corticosteroids. In contrast, the binding of AD to thymus DNA is not increased by cortisol. We propose that physiologically active corticosteroids mediate their permissive effects in cells by unmasking DNA sites in chromatin for attachment of natural signals or inducers.

REFERENCES

AMBROSE, C. T. (1964) *J. exp. Med.* **119**, 1027–1049.

AMBROSE, C. T. (1969) *J. exp. Med.* **130**, 1003–1029.

AMBROSE, C. T. (1970) *Fedn Proc. Fedn Am. Socs exp. Biol.* **29**(2), 470 (abst. 1267).

BERLINER, D. L. and DOUGHERTY, T. F. (1961) *Pharmac. Rev.* **13**, 329–359.

BONNER, J. and co-authors (1968) In *Methods in Enzymology*, vol. 12, *Nucleic Acids*, pt. B, pp. 3–65, ed. Grossman, L. and Moldave, K. New York: Academic Press.

BRUNKHORST, W. K. (1969) *Biochem. biophys. Res. Commun.* **35**, 880–886.

DAVIDSON, E. T., DEVENUTO, F. and WESTPHAL, U. (1963) *Proc. Soc. exp. Biol. Med.* **113**, 387–391.

FAGRAEUS, A. (1952) *Acta path. microbiol. scand.* suppl. 93, 20–28.

FUKUDA, T. R. (1952) *Jap. J. Physiol.* **2**, 208–212.

HECHTER, O. and JOHNSON, S. (1949) *Endocrinology* **45**, 351–369.

MICHAELIDES, M. C. and COONS, A. H. (1963) *J. exp. Med.* **117**, 1035–1051.

MIRICK, G. S. (1951) *Bull. Johns Hopkins Hosp.* **88**, 332–351.

OHTSUKA, E. and KOIDE, S. S. (1969) *Biochem. biophys. Res. Commun.* **35**, 648–652.

REICH, E. and GOLDBERG, I. H. (1964) *Recent Prog. Nucleic Acid Res. Molec. Biol.* **3**, 183–234.

RINGERTZ, N. R. and BOLUND, L. (1969) *Biochim. biophys. Acta* **174**, 147–154.

SANTÍSTEBAN, G. A. and DOUGHERTY, T. F. (1954) *Endocrinology* **54**, 130–146.

SLUYSER, M. (1969) *Biochim. biophys. Acta* **182**, 235–244.

STACKHOUSE, H. L., CHETSANGA, C. J. and TAN, C. H. (1968) *Biochim. biophys. Acta* **155**, 159–168.

TATA, J. R. (1966) *Recent Prog. Nucleic Acid Res. Molec. Biol.* **5**, 191–250.

VIES, J. VAN DER (1961) *Acta endocr.* **38**, 399–406.

DISCUSSION

Humphrey: You concluded by saying that cortisol may facilitate derepression. However, in your *in vitro* system will the secondary response occur without the antigen being present?

Ambrose: No. By emphasizing the absolute requirement for cortisol during induction of the immune response I didn't intend to minimize the cardinal role of antigen. Cortisol and antigen are equally essential to the inductive process. Primed lymph node fragments must be incubated with the priming antigen to elicit the secondary response; incubation for 2 hours with a suitable level of antigen is sufficient to elicit a maximal secondary response. Cortisol need not be present during this 2-hour exposure but must subsequently be available in the culture for the first 9 days to support an optimal response (see Fig. 3, p. 105).

Humphrey: Cultures which are stimulated for 2 hours with antigen on day 0 but not treated with cortisol until day 3 probably retain some antigen beyond this time because of its attachment to cell receptors. Is the response in such a culture dependent on the level of antigen persisting until the addition of cortisol? Is nothing happening in these cultures until you add cortisol?

Ambrose: The difficulty in answering such questions and in discussing cortisol's precise action is our poor understanding of the metabolic steps following antigen uptake by primed cells and preceding cell division and differentiation. For the sake of discussion we might classify cell division and differentiation as "secondary events" and define the "primary effect" as the effect(s) of antigen leading up to the secondary events. It seems likely that derepression is inherent in these two parts of the inductive process and that cortisol is intimately involved, therefore, in both. However, we have only inferential evidence that cortisol is essential for the secondary events. This evidence is derived from the following two sets of observations.

The secondary response is triggered off optimally on day 0, when the nodes are removed, the fragments prepared and the antigen added. Delay of this 2-hour antigen incubation until day 3 reduces the 21-day response elicited to 50 per cent or less of the optimal value and delay until day 6 reduces it to 10 per cent or less. Thus by day 6 the fragments have largely lost their capacity to be boosted. These observations should be compared with the following ones. Antigenic stimulation on day 0 yields an optimal 21-day response when 0·01 μM-cortisol is present in the medium for the first 9 days or longer (days 0–9 or days 0–21). The presence of cortisol for days 0–6 supports only about 50 per cent of the optimal response. Thus the presence of cortisol for the additional period of days 6–9 accounts for the remaining 50 per cent or so of the optimal response. This contribution to the total response by cortisol's presence during days 6–9 (50 per cent or so) contrasts with the meagre response elicited by antigen stimulation on day 6 (10 per cent or less). This difference suggests that cortisol facilitates secondary events precipitated by antigenic stimulation. Such events may include enzyme induction crucial for cell division and differentiation. These observations do not necessarily exclude cortisol's involvement in the primary effect of antigen, since this effect may be staggered over the first several days.

Korner: Are you in fact assuming that the response to cortisol is a specific one? Is it possible that cortisol is needed for some other metabolic activity of the cell without which it won't respond to antigen?

Ambrose: I suspect that in primed cells cortisol facilitates completion of a set of sequential metabolic events triggered off by re-exposure to the priming antigen. Since antibody production is the only index of the immune response that we follow, incompleteness of the secondary events prevents us from recognizing any primary antigenic effects. Until we can dissociate the primary antigenic effect from secondary events we cannot answer questions about which effect or event cortisol influences.

Humphrey: What is happening histologically during the inductive phase? Nine days is a long time.

Ambrose: The histological changes seen in lymph node cultures are similar to those noted in nodes boosted *in vivo*, both in the sequence of appearance and in the morphology of the antibody-containing cells (O'Brien, Michaelides and Coons 1964). These changes account for the exponential increase in antibody synthesis which occurs during the first 9 days or so (the inductive phase). After day 9 the antibody response either becomes linear for about a week or begins to decline, depending on factors not yet under our control. Thus by day 9 the cell population producing antibody apparently has stabilized or is beginning to die out.

Humphrey: Do you think there is a gradual recruitment of more cells during, say, the first three days so that the effect of added cortisol will be completed by the first four or five days?

Ambrose: I believe recruitment is somewhat slower but more protracted in these organ cultures than in lymph nodes boosted *in vivo*. This may partly explain why cortisol must be available to these cultures until day 9 to achieve a maximal response. As I mentioned before, cortisol's presence during days 6–9 accounts for 50 per cent or so of the total 21-day response.

Korner: If you have serum present, do you also have to add cortisol in order to get antibody formed?

Ambrose: A distinction should be made here between getting antibody formed and eliciting the secondary response. In cultures prepared from a recently primed animal a low level of antibody production may occur without the introduction of the antigen. This probably represents a waning primary response. The tissue culture work I described concerned only the induction of the secondary response *in vitro*. For this, physiological levels of cortisol are essential. Since most sera contain adequate levels of cortisol, medium containing such serum need not be supplemented with additional cortisol.

Korner: Could other components in the serum be responsible for supporting the secondary response in your cultures?

Ambrose: I doubt it. Serum-free media containing dialysates of serum support the inductive phase of the secondary response. So the crucial factor(s) in serum is a small dialysable molecule. Various physiologically active corticoids duplicate the effect of serum dialysates or whole serum. And so I see no basis for suspecting other serum components.

Korner: What about insulin?

Ambrose: Insulin in the serum-free medium is not essential for induction of the secondary response but its presence generally produces better sustained responses. This suggests that the lymph node fragments may have enough insulin initially but after a week or so in culture their dwindling intracellular insulin pool is profitably supplemented by exogenous insulin.

Korner: In the interpretation of your experiments on the effect of corticosteroids on the binding of actinomycin to chromatin, I recall a paper by Dahmus and Bonner (1965), who injected actinomycin and labelled corticosteroids into rats, and then separated out the nuclei from the liver. As they purified the nuclei, the chromatin and finally the DNA, they found less and less corticosteroid attached to these materials but more actinomycin was bound. They came to the conclusion that the steroid was not primarily going to the nucleus. Probably binding sites in the cytoplasm exist, rather like those for testosterone and oestrogens, and these may be the physiological binding sites.

Ambrose: I am not familiar with this paper but do recall that Dingman and Sporn (1965) obtained such results in normal rats. However, several more recent reports have reached different conclusions about the fate of injected labelled corticoids. Brunkhorst (1969) injected adrenalectomized rats intraperitoneally with [^{3}H]corticosterone and then fractionated their thymus cells at 15, 45 and 90-minute intervals. Radioactivity was initially high in the cytoplasmic fractions but decreased rapidly. In contrast, histone II (a fraction tightly bound to DNA) accumulated radioactivity over the time interval studied. Brunkhorst calculated that each nucleus contained approximately 1000 molecules of corticosterone. Sluyser (1966) had done similar experiments and had found labelled cortisol mainly bound to the lysine-poor histone fraction of rat liver. Finally, a recent paper from Sekeris's laboratory (Beato *et al.* 1970) presents evidence that a glycoprotein isolated from rat liver cytosol binds cortisol, transports this hormone into the nucleus, and thus facilitates its interaction with chromosomal proteins. The net effect is an increased transcription of rat liver chromatin.

Korner: Your results in the subcellular system are very nice, but is the effect a physiological one? Or is it a trick of the chemicals which enables actinomycin to bind better to DNA in the presence of steroid?

Ambrose: The data clearly show that cortisol increases the binding capacity of chromatin for actinomycin but not that of isolated DNA. The two titration schemes used in our studies measure the binding of actinomycin to DNA via guanine residues. No other type of binding in this system produces the same hypochromic shift in the absorption titration or the same decreased rotation in the optical rotation titration. So cortisol is not introducing some new spurious type of binding. The simplest explanation for these results is that cortisol interacts with the histone sheath of chromatin and unmasks guanine residues on the underlying DNA. The consistency between our organ culture data and the subcellular binding studies supports the hypothesis we propose, but obviously does not prove it.

Korner: I was interested in your finding that low concentrations ($<0\cdot01$ μM) of actinomycin D enhance antibody synthesis and in your hypothesis that this is due to inhibition of a messenger coding for the repressor, which presumably is more labile than the messenger for the antibody itself.

Ambrose: We have isolated from the used medium of our lymph node cultures a macromolecule which can inhibit a heterologous antibody–antigen system (Ambrose 1969). This inhibitory material is not specific antibody; it can be recovered only during the time that enhancement by actinomycin can be produced (days 6 to 15). These findings led us to propose that the immune response is controlled in part by such an antibody-inhibitory material and to suggest that many examples of antigenic competition are due to this phenomenon.

Korner: Are you suggesting that actinomycin can inhibit synthesis of a messenger for antibody at one dosage and can inhibit the synthesis of a messenger for a repressor protein specific for antibody at a much lower dosage? Actinomycin does many things other than inhibit RNA synthesis. Is it not possible to explain your data by suggesting that some doses of actinomycin facilitate movement of certain messengers from nucleus to cytoplasm?

Ambrose: Your initial question is exactly what I am suggesting, for there are numerous examples in the literature of the differential susceptibility of various messenger RNAs to actinomycin D. This literature has never been summarized, to my knowledge, and so I might give a few examples here. In *Bacillus subtilis* treated with a given level of actinomycin Pollock (1963) observed a 46 per cent increase in penicillinase level but progressively larger decreases for β-galactosidase, α-amylase and α-glucosidase. In another strain of *B. subtilis* Kadowaki, Hosoda and Maruo (1965) found that actinomycin produced only slight inhibition of ribonuclease but strong inhibition of alkaline phosphatase and α-amylase. Yamada and Kawamata (1966) suggested that mRNA synthesis might be inhibited by actinomycin D in proportion to the size of its cistron. The two examples I just cited are consistent with this suggestion. There are many other examples of differential susceptibility to actinomycin. Unfortunately, I don't know examples of actinomycin controlling the movement of messengers from nucleus to cytoplasm.

Korner: Have you tested whether those steroids which you found to be inhibitory (progesterone or testosterone) affect the increased binding of actinomycin by chromatin treated with cortisol?

Ambrose: No, I haven't yet. I won't be surprised if no competitive effect is demonstrable in the subcellular system, since this effect in the organ cultures may be a membrane phenomenon. Parenthetically, I might add that I hope to determine whether organ specificity for different steroids can be shown with the chromatin–actinomycin titration system and whether, for example, progesterone increases actinomycin binding to uterine chromatin but not to chromatin from other organs on which progesterone has no physiological effect.

King: There is one snag in your interpretation of the binding data. You obtained stimulation of antibody production *in vitro* at 10^{-8} M-cortisol and inhibition at 10^{-6} M. Yet the concentration needed for an increase in binding of actinomycin D by chromatin was substantially greater (50 μM or 5×10^{-5} M)—that is, well above the concentration which inhibits antibody production. At this concentration of cortisol you are approaching the level at which it will saturate a water-hydrocarbon interface (10 μM, 10^{-5} M) (Munck 1957, 1965). Is it not possible that the increased actinomycin-binding capacity produced by cortisol is just a detergent action of the steroid opening up DNA binding sites?

Ambrose: Let me summarize the relevant facts from our studies. Induction of the secondary response *in vitro* is supported by a broad range of cortisol concentrations. A moderate supportive effect is seen with levels as low as 0·001 μM (10^{-9} M), but the optimal supporting range is 0·01–1·0 μM (10^{-8}–10^{-6} M). Slight inhibition is produced by 10 μM (10^{-5} M) and about 50 per cent inhibition by 100 μM (10^{-4} M). So your concern over the 50 μM level used in the subcellular binding studies is understandable. However, the amount of chromatin or isolated DNA we used in a titration is enormous relative to the amount contained in the lymph node fragments of a culture. If regarded in this light, 50 μM is not an unreasonably high concentration.

I doubt that a non-specific detergent action is the mechanism at work in the subcellular binding studies, since equimolar levels of 11-epicortisol, tetrahydrocortisol and 11-epicorticosterone produce no increase in the binding capacity of chromatin for actinomycin. On the other hand, corticosterone, the major adrenal steroid of the rabbit, produces an effect on binding comparable to cortisol. A non-specific detergent effect would be produced by all steroids and not just the physiologically active ones, as was the case here.

King: A concentration of 50 μM is still 1000-fold higher than the level of corticosteroids normally present in the blood.

Ambrose: Yes; this discrepancy requires some explanation. We might speculate that during the isolation of the chromatin certain binding factors are lost which in the intact cell permit more efficient use of the thousand or so cortisol molecules reaching the nucleus.

King: Ohtsuka and Koide (1969) measured the effect of several corticosteroids on the template activity of *fragmented* liver nuclei obtained from adrenalectomized rats. They found that 21-dehydrocortisol stimulated RNA synthesis much more than did cortisol.

Ambrose: They suggested that 21-dehydrocortisol may be the active form of the steroid to which cortisol must first be converted. They also noted that 21-dehydrocortisol was less effective than cortisol in stimulating RNA polymerase activity of *intact* rat liver nuclei and concluded that the 21-dehydro derivative may be hindered in its transport into the nucleus. In our organ culture system 21-dehydrocortisol is only slightly less active on a molar basis than cortisol. We have not tested this derivative in a subcellular titration system for its effect on actinomycin binding to chromatin. I should add here that cortisol-increased template activity was also reported for rat liver nuclei by Dukes, Sekeris and Schmid (1966) and for rat liver chromatin by Stackhous, Chetsanga and Tan (1968). However, Monder and Walker (1970) have been unable to confirm these reports in isolated rat liver and thymus nuclei using both cortisol and 21-dehydrocortisol.

Pierpaoli: Ballard and Tomkins (1969) have studied the induction by cortisol of the synthesis of tyrosine aminotransferase in hepatoma cells in tissue culture. They have also studied the effect of cortisol on the membranes of these cells. It seems that cortisol induces the formation of a factor on the cell membrane which increases the capacity of the cells to adhere to the glass in which the cells are cultured. There are therefore at least two further possible effects of the hormone in your system, besides the one you mentioned. Firstly, an effect on the cell membrane may be important, because conservation of the structure of the tissue fragments and of the connexions between the connective tissue network and the parenchyme seems to be a prerequisite for maintaining the capacity of the tissue to produce antibody. The hormone would prevent dedifferentiation of cells and tissues. Secondly, an effect on the membrane may also be important for what you call the inductive phase of antibody production, because of contact with the antigen, or its uptake. The modification induced by antigen at the membrane or alternatively the action of cortisol on the cell membrane before or after contact with antigen may not require any action of cortisol on the DNA.

Ambrose: I discussed the structural and functional integrity of the lymph node organ cultures in some detail previously (Ambrose 1964). In our cultures serum promotes cell emigration, disintegration of the architecture of the lymph node fragments, and early decline in the fragments' antibody production. Cortisol has been reported to retard cell migration in various cultures (reviewed in Ambrose 1964). However, I doubt that cortisol exerts a significant effect of this sort in our organ cultures. Instead, I believe the more prolonged antibody synthesis we find in serum-free medium containing cortisol is due to the absence of serum and not the presence of cortisol.

We have examined repeatedly the question of whether cortisol exerts an effect on antigen uptake or at least on some early aspect of antigenic stimulation. In our culture system a clear dose–response effect on the subsequent antibody response can be shown with different levels of antigen during the 2-hour incubation on day 0. We tested a range of antigen concentrations with two extreme levels of cortisol ($0 \cdot 02$ μM and $2 \cdot 0$ μM)—both of which support good antibody responses when an optimal antigen concentration is used. In four out of five experiments the higher level of cortisol made the different antigen concentrations no more effective than they were in the presence of the lower cortisol concentration. So I cannot confirm your suspicions that cortisol may facilitate some effect of antigen at the membrane level.

REFERENCES

AMBROSE, C. T. (1964) In *Retention of Functional Differentiation in Cultured Cells* (Wistar Institute Monograph No. 1), pp. 71–86. Philadelphia: The Wistar Institute.

AMBROSE, C. T. (1969) *J. exp. Med.* **130,** 1003–1029.

BALLARD, P. L. and TOMKINS, G. M. (1969) *Nature, Lond.* **224,** 344–345.

BEATO, M., BRÄNDLE, W., BIESEWIG, D. and SEKERIS, C. E. (1970) *Biochim. biophys. Acta* **208,** 125–136.

BRUNKHORST, W. K. (1969) *Biochem: biophys. Res. Commun.* **35,** 880–886.

DAHMUS, M. E. and BONNER, J. (1965) *Proc. natn. Acad. Sci. U.S.A.* **54,** 1370–1375.

DINGMAN, C. W. and SPORN, M. B. (1965) *Science* **149,** 1251–1254.

DUKES, P. P., SEKERIS, C. E. and SCHMID, W. (1966) *Biochim. biophys. Acta* **123,** 126–133.

KADOWAKI, K., HOSODA, J. and MARUO, B. (1965) *Biochim. biophys. Acta* **103,** 311–318.

MONDER, C. and WALKER, M. C. (1970) *Biochemistry* **9,** 2489–2497.

MUNCK, A. (1957) *Biochim. biophys. Acta* **24,** 507–514.

MUNCK, A. (1965) *Endocrinology* **77,** 356–360.

O'BRIEN, T. F., MICHAELIDES, M. C. and COONS, A. H. (1964) *J. exp. Med.* **117,** 1053–1062.

OHTSUKA, E. and KOIDE, S. S. (1969) *Biochem. biophys. Res. Commun.* **35,** 648–652.

POLLOCK, M. R. (1963) *Biochim. biophys. Acta* **76,** 80–93.

SLUYSER, M. (1966) *J. molec. Biol.* **19,** 591–595.

STACKHOUSE, H. L. CHETSANGA, C. J. and TAN, C. H. (1968) *Biochim. biophys. Acta* **155,** 159–168.

YAMADA, T. and KAWAMATA, J. (1966) *Biken's J.* **9,** 125–130.

DEVELOPMENTAL HORMONES AND IMMUNOLOGICAL MATURATION

W. PIERPAOLI,[*] N. FABRIS AND E. SORKIN

Medizinische Abteilung, Schweizerisches Forschungsinstitut, Davos-Platz

IT has been reported in previous publications from our laboratory (Pierpaoli and Sorkin 1967a, 1969a, b; Pierpaoli et al. 1969) and by others (Ambrose 1964; Hollander, Takakura and Yamada 1968) that hormones influence the development and performance of the immune system. There is also abundant clinical evidence for the importance of hormones in immunity (Fisher 1964). Immunologically competent lymphocytes are believed to derive from bone marrow cells which acquire immunological responsiveness through some action of the thymus. It is one of the main theses of this paper that processes of maturation and differentiation in the thymus and in thymus-derived tissues are under hormonal regulation and that the adenohypophysis controls these processes. Our present work is concerned with the action of some developmental hormones, such as somatotropin or growth hormone (STH) and thyroxine, on the maturation and expression of the immunological capacity. We shall discuss a number of experimental and hypothetical points about the significance of hormones in the ontogeny and maintenance of a functional immune system.

FIG. 1. Electron micrograph of "thymotropic" acidophilic cells (T-STH) with dilatation of the cisternae of the endoplasmic reticulum in the adenohypophysis removed from neonatally thymectomized NMRI mice.

(a) Adenohypophysis 33 days after neonatal thymectomy, showing thymotropic cells. × 4800. (b) Adenohypophysis of normal sham-operated littermate of same age, showing normal acidophilic cells (STH). × 4800.

(c) Adenohypophysis 30 days after neonatal thymectomy. One thymotropic cell. × 10 000. (d) Adenohypophysis of normal sham-operated littermate of same age. One normal acidophilic cell. × 10 000.

(Electron micrographs taken by Dr Elena Bianchi, University of Pavia, Italy.)

*Research fellow of the National Research Council, Rome, Italy.

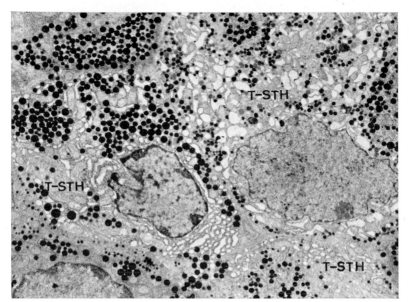

FIG. 1a.

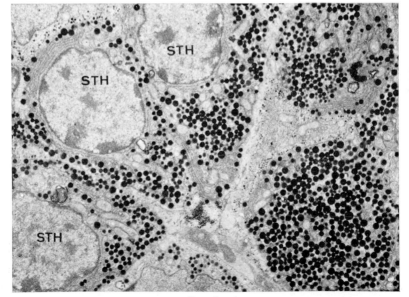

FIG. 1b.

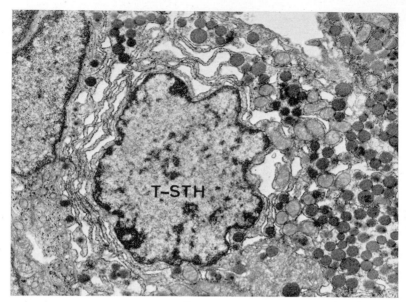

FIG. 1C.

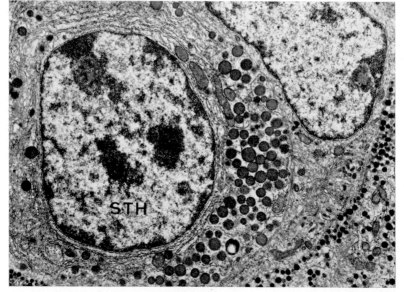

FIG. 1d.

(1) THE PERINATAL THYMUS IS A TARGET ORGAN OF THE ADENOHYPOPHYSIS

There is evidence for the relationship between the thymus and the hypophysis. Pierpaoli and Sorkin (1967a, 1968) have described studies on the induction of wasting disease with thymus and spleen atrophy after treatment with rabbit anti-mouse-hypophysis serum or anti-bovine STH serum in young adult mice. On the other hand, if the thymus is a classical target organ of the adenohypophysis we should expect changes in the hypophysis such as are observed after extirpation of other target glands. We have demonstrated by both light microscopy (Pierpaoli and Sorkin 1967b) and electron microscopy (Fig. 1) that a degranulation of the acidophilic, growth hormone-producing cells occurs in the adenohypophysis of mice after neonatal thymectomy. Fig. 2 shows the increasing number of enlarged degranulated cells in the mouse anterior pituitary at increasing times after thymectomy at birth. These modifications in the number of acidophilic cells with confluent cisternae of the dilated endoplasmic reticulum ("thymotropic cells") are a manifestation of an increased demand for and output of the hormone from the cells after solubilization of the hormone granules in the Golgi apparatus. No such modifications were observed by optical microscopy in mice thymectomized as young adults (Pierpaoli and Sorkin 1967b) or in neonatally splenectomized mice. These results demonstrate the interdependence between the perinatal thymus and the STH-producing cells in the hypophysis.

Other recent evidence derives from experiments on autosomal recessive dwarf mice with a deficient pituitary. The thymus and lymph nodes of these mice are extremely depleted of lymphoid cells (Baroni 1967; Pierpaoli et al. 1969, see section 2 below). This evidence supports the proposition that the thymus is a target organ of the adenohypophysis. It suggests but does not finally answer the question of whether somatotropic hormone is the thymotropic hormone.

(2) SOMATOTROPIC HORMONE IS A THYMOTROPIC HORMONE

The thymus is doubtless subjected to the influence of several endocrine glands (Comsa 1961; Dougherty et al. 1964; Ernström and Larsson 1965). Some of the evidence for a major role of STH during the development of the thymus-dependent immune system has been summarized above. The sensitivity of the thymus to STH has been tested by various means. Following the findings that anti-mouse hypophysis serum results in lymphocyte depletion

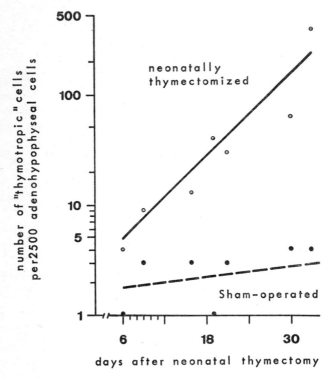

FIG. 2. Number of "thymotropic" acidophilic cells in the adenohypophysis of neonatally thymectomized NMRI mice and sham-operated littermates at various times after operation.

of thymus and spleen, we prepared antisera to bovine STH (Raben type; mouse STH is not available) and injected them into mice (Pierpaoli and Sorkin 1968). The recipients of these anti-STH sera showed similar lymphocyte depletion in the thymus cortex and in thymus-dependent areas of the spleen to that observed with anti-hypophysis sera.

In other experiments the Snell-Bagg hypopituitary dwarf mice served as a model. These mice produce only about a thousandth of the amount of STH produced by their normal littermates (Garcia and Geschwind 1968). Their thymuses and lymph nodes are practically devoid of lymphocytes (Baroni 1967); they show normal immunoglobulin levels (Wilkinson, Singh and Sorkin 1970) and reject foreign skin grafts at between 20 and 40 days; that is, with a mean retardation of about 15 days (Fabris, Pierpaoli and Sorkin 1970). They die within 45–150 days after birth, depending on their habitat. When 30-day-old Snell-Bagg dwarf mice were given STH, thyroxine, or STH and thyroxine together, their thymus and lymph nodes became fully repopulated with lymphocytes (Pierpaoli et al. 1969). The production of antibodies to sheep red cells and homograft rejection, which were both delayed before hormone treatment, became normal.

These experiments are conclusive evidence that STH is a thymotropic hormone. It influences the cellularity of all lymphoid tissues. One open question concerns the purity of the STH preparations. It is conceivable that traces of other pituitary hormones are present in these bovine preparations. However, the clear finding that the acidophilic cells in the pituitary degranulate after thymectomy speaks in favour of our assumption (2). It does not exclude, however, the possibility that other hormones are acting on the thymus or that STH exerts its effect on the thymus indirectly through hormones of other target glands.

(3) IMMUNOLOGICAL MATURATION DEPENDS ON ENDOCRINOLOGICAL FUNCTION

This is the main and crucially important proposition. The parallelism of immunological and endocrinological immaturity in newborn and young rodents suggested to us the possibility of a causal relation between the two systems for the maturation of the immune capacity. Light microscopic examination of the adenohypophysis and the level of somatotropic hormone in the pituitary gland of rodents in the perinatal period (Siperstein et al. 1954; Daughaday et al. 1968), as well as our previous findings on the dependence of thymo–lymphatic tissue development on some pituitary hormones, seem compatible with this assumption.

Although STH and other hormones most likely act on antibody-producing plasma cells, for example in polyribosomal synthesis, we assume that one of its main actions lies in the control of the development of a thymus-dependent lymphocyte population. This hormonal dependence of the onset of immunological reactivity during ontogenesis and perinatal life has been evaluated by testing the effect of hormones on donor cells in modifying the course of the graft-versus-host (GVH) reaction (Simonsen 1962) and runt disease. Spleen cells or thymocytes from adult or newborn mice were inoculated together with hormones into normal or thymectomized newborn or a few-days-old mice of a histo-

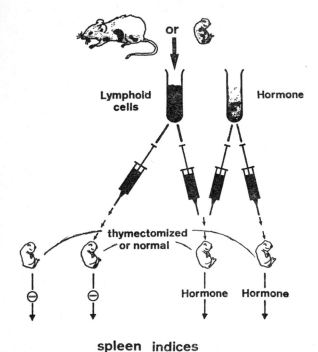

spleen indices

Fig. 3. Diagram to illustrate the experimental model used to evaluate the effect of hormones on the immunocompetence of cells in the graft-versus-host assay.

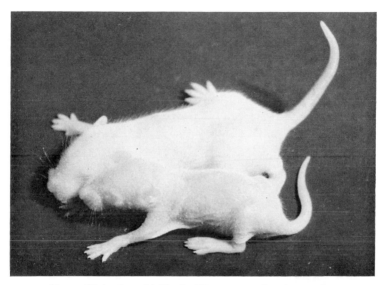

FIG. 4. Eight-day-old Charles River mouse showing runting after one intravenous injection at birth of 5×10^6 spleen cells from an adult C3H donor; 100 μg STH and 0·1 μg thyroxine were injected for 7 days. Control littermate injected with cells only.

incompatible strain or into the F_1 hybrid of the donor and recipient strain (Fig. 3).

(a) *Injection of spleen cells and hormones into newborn histoincompatible mice or rats influences the course of runt disease*

Five to 10×10^6 spleen cells from young adult male C3H mice were injected intravenously into newborn Charles River (CR) recipients. Mice of the same litter were treated for seven or eight days with daily doses of 100 μg somatotropic hormone (STH) and 0·1–0·5 μg thyroxine. Mice treated with both hormones and cells developed an accelerated runt disease and died within 7 to 15 days of age (Fig. 4). Mice injected only with spleen cells developed runt disease a few days later, but some of them eventually recovered. Mice injected with hormone alone grew normally.

The same type of experiment was done using 4-week-old Long Evans rats as cell donors and as recipients, newborn Charles River rats. The newborn rats were injected intraperitoneally with 30×10^6 spleen cells, and some of them were treated with 200 μg STH and 0·5 μg thyroxine. Some controls were treated with hormones alone. In this combination of strains the rats injected with only cells or hormones grew normally, while those treated with both spleen cells and hormones developed a runt disease. The pathological changes were those described in classical runt disease (Billingham 1968). The above evidence suggests therefore that the graft-versus-host reaction has been influenced by STH and thyroxine and results in the development of runt disease.

(b) *STH increases the potential of adult allogeneic mouse spleen cells to induce a GVH response in newborns*

The GVH test has been used to determine whether the effect of the hormones in inducing runt disease was not due to a direct action of the hormone on the lymphatic tissues of the recipient. C3H mice were used as donors when newborn Charles River mice were the recipients. Adult CR or C3H mice were used as donors when $(CR \times C3H)F_1$ hybrids were used as recipients. A striking increase of spleen size in mice injected with both spleen cells and STH was noted (Fig. 5). Whether STH influenced the immunocompetence of the injected allogeneic spleen cells or cells of one parental strain or whether it induced them to

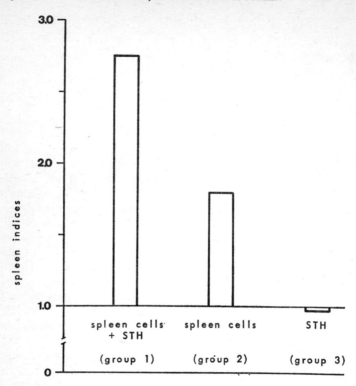

Fig. 5. Graft-versus-host reaction (spleen indices) in (C3H × CR)F$_1$ hybrid mice injected once intraperitoneally, at birth, with 10 × 10^6 spleen cells from 4-week-old C3H donors. Daily doses of 100 μg STH were given for 9 days. Mice were killed on day 9.

divide is unknown. The same type of experiment performed by injecting syngeneic cells did not show any specific STH-induced activation of the injected spleen cells.

(c) *STH induces immunocompetence in thymocytes of newborn and adult mice*

While the experiments in (a) and (b) showed significant effects of STH on adult spleen cells they left open the crucial question of its action on cells of newborn, immunologically incompetent donors. In order to evaluate the effect of hormones on the maturation of thymus cells of newborn or adult mice, we injected cells from one parental strain of $(C_3H \times CR)F_1$ hybrids into newborn or a few-days-old $(C_3H \times CR)F_1$ hybrid recipients. The experimental conditions were similar to those in (b). As shown in Fig. 6A, STH strongly potentiates the weak capacity of thymocytes to induce a GVH response or even renders them capable of behaving as immunocompetent cells when their injection is followed by treatment with STH. The use of thymocytes from newborn donors makes it unlikely that the cell inocula contained immunocompetent cells from peripheral blood.

The capacity of certain developmental hormones to change immunologically non-reactive or weakly reactive cells of newborns into efficient effector cells in a graft-versus-host reaction suggested at first that these hormones act through the thymus of the recipient. However, neonatally thymectomized recipients behaved in an identical manner, as is shown below. It is therefore likely that these hormones act directly in some way on the transferred cells.

(d) STH induces competence in thymocytes from newborn donors in the absence of the recipient thymus

The question of whether the effect of STH was exerted directly on the injected thymocytes without the need of the recipient thymus was evaluated as follows. F_1 hybrid recipients were thymectomized at 1–4 days of age, and at days 6–8 they were injected with 5–10×10^6 thymocytes from one of the newborn parental strains. Fig. 6B indicates that the GVH response can be induced in thymectomized recipients just as well as in the normal ones, thus ruling out the participation of the host thymus in the process of differentiation or maturation of the injected cells by the hormone.

The historadioautographic technique with tritiated thymidine (Radiochemical Centre, Amersham, England: specific activity 10 000 μC/mM) was used in similar experiments to evaluate the variation of mitotic activity in the spleen of the recipient mice injected with thymocytes alone, hormone alone, both cells and hormone, or of untreated controls. The results are illustrated in Fig. 7. The increased number of labelled spleen cells when both cells and hormone were injected indicate that the somatotropic

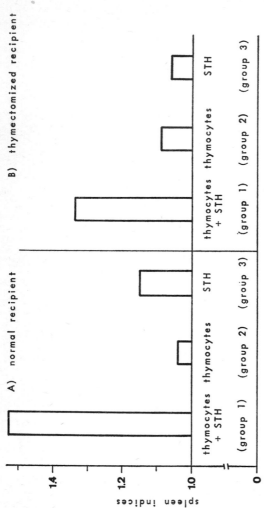

Fig. 6 (A) (*left*). Somatotropic hormone-induced immunocompetence in Charles River mouse thymocytes. Assay: GVH response (spleen indices) in normal (C3H × CR)F₁ hybrid mice. Groups 1 and 2 were injected at 2 days after birth with 5 × 10⁶ thymocytes from newborn Charles River donors. Groups 1 and 3 received 100 μg STH daily for 10 days. One group remained untreated. Mice were killed at day 12.

(B) (*right*). STH-induced immunocompetence in Charles River mouse thymocytes. Assay: GVH response (spleen indices) in (C3H × CR)F₁ hybrid mice thymectomized at 4 days of age. Groups 1 and 2 were injected at day 5 with 5 × 10⁶ thymocytes from newborn Charles River donors. Groups 1 and 3 received 100 μg STH daily for 10 days. One group remained untreated. Mice were killed at day 15.

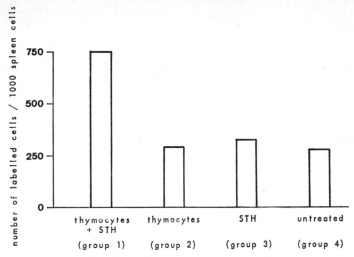

FIG. 7. STH-induced immunocompetence in thymocytes. Historadioautography of spleen cells of neonatally thymectomized CR recipient mice. Groups 1 and 2 received at day 1, 5×10^6 thymocytes of adult C3H donors. Groups 1 and 3 received 100 µg STH daily. Group 4 was untreated. All mice were killed on day 4. [³H]thymidine, 0·8 µg/g body weight, was injected into all groups 1 hour before killing. Results evaluated as number of labelled cells per 1000 spleen cells counted.

hormone has enhanced the capacity of the injected thymocytes to induce a graft-versus-host reaction.

(e) *The hormonal reconstitution of dwarf mice results in long-lasting immunocompetence*

It was found that after dwarf mice had been reconstituted with STH and thyroxine for 4 weeks, and after a rest period of 2 months, the 4-month-old mice could still reject a foreign skin graft in the normal time of 12–15 days. While many untreated dwarf mice died between 40–150 days, some of the reconstituted dwarf mice have in fact survived for over a year and one such mouse is now 450 days old. This may mean that these mice also have a high level of cellular and presumably humoral immunity. The evidence suggests that the hormones most probably created a long-lived lymphocyte population which out-lived the hormone action itself. The very low level of hormones produced by the dwarfs may suffice, however, to maintain the level of immuno-competent cells and to produce antibodies in adult life.

All the above experiments indicate that STH is a thymotropic hormone which is directly responsible, possibly with the coopera-tion of other hormones, for the transformation of thymocytes into immunocompetent cells which are active in cell-mediated immune reactions, such as the graft-versus-host response. Apparently no factors are needed from the recipient thymus for the development of cells active in such delayed-type immune reactions. Although the role of other hormones cannot be excluded, the experimental facts illustrate that the immunological function of the thymus cells and thymus-derived cells can be fully expressed only in the presence of somatotropic hormone. These data are in full agreement with our previous findings (Pier-paoli and Sorkin 1969a, b) and views on the significance of the thymus–pituitary axis (Pierpaoli and Sorkin 1967a).

A most salient point is the fact that thymocytes of a newborn animal under the influence of injected STH can evoke a cell-mediated immune reaction in another newborn animal. The recipient, being an F_1 hybrid, is incapable of reacting against these thymocytes. The presumable explanation for this is that the newborn recipient is endocrinologically and immuno-logically immature and cannot therefore react against the foreign thymocytes. Even if the injected hormone caused maturation in the recipient, as it presumably does of the donor cells, it would be incapable of mounting a host-versus-graft reaction, since it is a histocompatible hybrid. Since the newborn recipients were thymectomized these same experiments seem also to indicate that the STH-induced immunocompetence of the donor thymo-cytes is not mediated through the release of a hypothetical thymus factor by the recipients. It is possible that STH is acting on the thymocytes of the donor through thymosin (Goldstein et al. 1970).

(4) SIGNIFICANCE OF INTERRELATION OF STH WITH INSULIN AND THYROXINE FOR IMMUNOLOGICAL FUNCTION

This problem has been previously investigated (Pierpaoli and Sorkin 1969a; Pierpaoli et al. 1969) by evaluating the effect of hormones on the lymphoid tissues or by the deficiencies produced by their absence or low levels. The known dependence of the activity of STH-producing cells on thyroid function (Purves and Griesbach 1946; Solomon and Greep 1959; Daughaday *et al*. 1968) was studied by using rabbit anti-bovine thyrotropic hormone serum. When this serum was repeatedly injected into young adult mice, it induced a striking involution of the spleen in spite of its own strong antigenicity, and antibody formation was reduced or absent (Pierpaoli and Sorkin 1969a). STH treatment of these mice, whose thyroid function was impaired or reduced, produced a striking reconstitution of the peripheral lymphoid tissues, particularly in the perifollicular zones of the lymphoid follicles and in the thymus-dependent areas of the spleen.

Another experimental system was used to evaluate the dependence of STH on thyroxine and the role of STH in the immune response. Mice and rats were treated with propyl-thiouracil (PTU), which is known to block release of thyroxine. Treatment of these animals with PTU for 20 days produces a decrease in the relative spleen weight, while the relative thymus weight is not changed by comparison with the untreated controls. The primary immune response to sheep red blood cells is greatly impaired. A full reversal and recovery from these conditions can be obtained by injecting the PTU-treated animals with thyroxine or STH, the latter hormone giving an even more complete reconstitution in size and morphological appearance of the spleen and of the primary immune response to sheep red cells (Fig. 8). These actions of STH support the proposition that STH is the hormone responsible for the differentiation of lymphocytes into antibody-forming cells and/or for the actual performance of the latter.

The well-known interrelationship between STH and insulin has also been evaluated, as far as the delayed-type immune response is concerned, by using the graft-versus-host assay described in section (3). Injection of STH and insulin or of insulin alone, in combination with thymocytes or spleen cells, into $(C_3H \times CR)F_1$ hybrids induces a spleen enlargement which, however, does not seem specific for immunological function because it can be induced by the hormone alone. This shows that insulin, although strongly active in metabolic processes and in

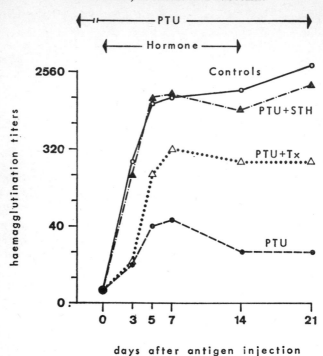

FIG. 8. Reversal of depressed antibody production to sheep red cells in propyl-thiouracil (PTU)-treated young adult rats by STH or thyroxine. Thyroid function was blocked by 20 days' treatment with PTU. Hormones were given for 14 days, beginning at the time of antigenic challenge.

inducing enlargement of the spleen, does not influence the immunocompetence of the injected spleen cells or thymocytes.

(5) THE MOST CRITICAL EFFECT OF HORMONES IS DURING THE DEVELOPMENT OF THE IMMUNE SYSTEM

Although developmental hormones are present and acting during the whole life of a mammal, we assume that their influence on immunological function is more essential at the time of its ontogenetic development than in the maintenance of an already fully developed immune system. Our assumption is based on the following facts.

(a) Anti-pituitary serum induces wasting disease only when given in the first weeks of life; when given later it does not produce any impairment of cellular immunity.

(b) Cellular and humoral immunity deficiencies can be observed in dwarf mice, whose hypopituitary condition is present already at birth. Reconstituted dwarf mice can survive many months without losing the immunological functions acquired by the hormonal treatment. Similarly, rats hypophysectomized as adults do not show any immunological deficiencies.

(c) Removal of some endocrine glands in rats gives different results depending on whether the operation is performed in adults or in 7-day-old animals. For example, thyroidectomy in adult animals produces only a slight decrease in peripheral white blood cells, while the relative weight of the thymus and skin graft survival are unmodified (Fig. 9). If thyroidectomy is

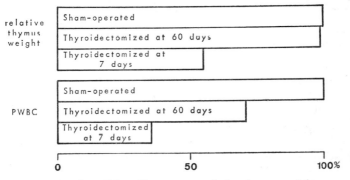

FIG. 9. Effect of thyroidectomy on relative thymus weight and peripheral white blood cells (PWBC) in Charles River rats. The animals were operated at 7 or 60 days of age or sham-operated. Tests performed at 30 days after operation.

performed in 7-day-old animals, it produces a large decrease in relative thymus weight and in peripheral white blood cells and a significant delay of skin graft survival (Fig. 10).

(d) As is suggested by the experiments with the graft-versus-host model (see section 3c), thymocytes of newborn animals need hormones to acquire their immune capacity.

It should be noted, however, that maturation and differentiation of immunocompetent cells takes place during the whole lifespan.

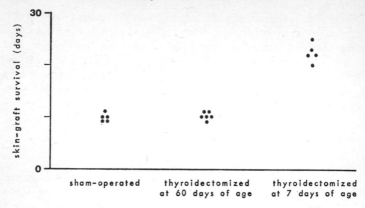

FIG. 10. Effect of thyroidectomy on skin graft survival
in Charles River rats. The animals were operated at 7 or 60
days of age or sham-operated. Skin from Long-Evans
donor rats was grafted 30 days after the operation.

This has been demonstrated by the appearance of immunological
deficiencies many months after adult thymectomy or by the
impairment of immunological recovery from X-irradiation by
animals thymectomized in adult life (Miller 1965; Metcalf 1965;
Taylor 1965). In agreement with these observations, recent
findings (Duquesnoy, Mariani and Good 1969; our unpublished
data) have shown that the immunological recovery of X-irradiated
animals or animals given large doses of cortisol is dependent on
the presence of certain endocrine glands. These facts provide
further evidence that some hormones are needed for maturation
and differentiation of immunocompetent cells, irrespective of the
age at which such functional maturation takes place.

DISCUSSION

The experimental data strengthen our view that some hormones,
amongst them chiefly somatotropic hormone, strongly influence
or even determine some maturational steps of the immunolymphatic tissue.

Virtually nothing is known yet about the hormone sensitivity
of lymphoid cells at various stages of their development nor is it
clear whether these hormones are mainly promoting lymphocyte
proliferation or cell differentiation. It is also conceivable that the

regulation of the thymus and thymus-derived cells is subjected to a different hormonal control from other lymphoid cell populations. Evidence for this view comes from our previous work (Pierpaoli and Sorkin 1968, 1969a; Pierpaoli *et al.* 1969), work by Mueller, Wolfe and Meyer (1960) and Warner and Burnet (1961) using testosterone in chickens, and by Sherman and Dameshek (1964) employing testosterone and oestrogens in hamsters.

How far antigen modifies the hormone sensitivity of lymphoid cells needs also to be determined. Whether somatotropic hormone acts directly on lymphatic tissue or whether its action is mediated through other hormones is unknown.

The use of *in vivo* and *in vitro* systems, in which the specific stage of the hormone dependence of the precursors of antigen-sensitive cells could be established, might permit the identification of a cell population whose evolution needs the presence of some hormones at a certain stage of its differentiation. The debated question of morphological or anatomical cell compartmentation might then be solved on the basis of cellular hormone dependence.

The demonstration that STH strongly influences the development of lymphoid cells which determine delayed hypersensitivities, such as was shown in the reconstitution of dwarf mice, or the STH-induced maturation of newborn thymocytes, suggests new possibilities for the control of a mature immune system.

The ontogenetic approach—that is, the experimental possibility of influencing the functional capacity of lymphoid organs at an early stage of formation—combined with studies on the timing, sequence and mechanisms of action of hormones on the thymo-lymphatic immune system, should eventually permit the development of means to control the adult functional and mature immune system. It opens up a new unexploited means of influencing immunological reactions. Interfering with the processes of immunological maturation with anti-hormone sera, anti-pituitary sera or ideally with specific chemical inhibitors of hormones, might be a new approach to solving the problem of organ transplantation.

SUMMARY

Several propositions have been made on the relation between endocrinological function and immunological maturation and expression of the immune capacity. The perinatal thymus is a target organ of the adenohypophysis. After neonatal thymectomy, thymotropic acidophilic cells in the anterior pituitary were detected by light and electron microscopy. Somatotropic hormone (STH) is a thymotropic hormone, as verified by the STH-sensitivity of the thymus. STH may act directly on thymus cells or by mediating the release of another factor (thymosin?) from these target cells in the manner of a classical hypophysis–target organ relationship. Immunological maturation seems to depend on endocrine function, as was shown by runt disease induced by STH and thyroxine and spleen cells in newborn mice and rats. STH when given together with thymocytes of newborn C3H or Charles River mice produces a graft-versus-host reaction in $(C3H \times CR)F_1$ hybrids. The hormone presumably induced immunocompetence in the thymocytes of the newborn donors. Experiments using immunologically deficient hypopituitary dwarf mice suggest that after reconstitution with STH a long-lasting effective cellular immunity is established. Inhibition of thyroid function by antithyrotropic hormone or propyl-thiouracil results in changes in lymphoid tissues and impairment of the immune response. These effects can be reversed by STH or thyroxine. The most critical effect of hormones is at the time of ontogeny of the immune system, but developmental hormones presumably exercise their action throughout the entire mammalian life.

Acknowledgement

This work was supported by the Schweizerische Nationalfonds zur Förderung der wissenschaftlichen Forschung (Grant 3.246.69 SR).

REFERENCES

AMBROSE, C. T. (1964) *J. exp. Med.* **119**, 1027–1049.

BARONI, C. (1967) *Experientia* **23**, 282–283.

BILLINGHAM, R. E. (1968) *Harvey Lect.* **62**, 21–78.

COMSA, J. (1961) *Pflügers Arch. ges. Physiol.* **272**, 562–574.

DAUGHADAY, W. H., PEAKE, G. T., BIRGE, C. A. and MARIZ, I. K. (1968) In *Growth Hormone*, pp. 238–252, ed. Pecile, A. and Müller, E. E. Amsterdam: Excerpta Medica Foundation. (International Congress Series No. 158).

DOUGHERTY, T. F., BERLINER, M. L., SCHNEEBELI, G. L. and BERLINER, D. L. (1964) *Ann. N.Y. Acad. Sci.* **113**, 825–843.

DUQUESNOY, R. J., MARIANI, T. and GOOD, R. A. (1969) *Proc. Soc. exp. Biol. Med.* **132**, 1176–1178.

ERNSTRÖM, U. and LARSSON, B. (1965) *Acta physiol. scand.* **64,** 426–433.

FABRIS, N., PIERPAOLI, W. and SORKIN, E. (1970) In *Developmental Aspects of Antibody Formation and Structure.* Prague: Publishing House of the Czechoslovak Academy of Sciences. In press.

FISHER, E. R. (1964) In *The Thymus in Immunobiology*, pp. 676–717, ed. Good, R. A. and Gabrielsen, A. E. New York: Harper.

GARCIA, J. F. and GESCHWIND, I. I. (1968) In *Growth Hormone*, pp. 267–291, ed. Pecile, A. and Müller, E. E. Amsterdam: Excerpta Medica Foundation. (International Congress Series No. 158.)

GOLDSTEIN, A. L., ASANUMA, Y., BATTISTO, J. R., HARDY, M. A., QUINT, J. and WHITE, A. (1970) *J. Immun.* **104,** 359–366.

HOLLANDER, V. P., TAKAKURA, K. and YAMADA, H. (1968) *Recent Prog. Horm. Res.* **24,** 81–131.

METCALF, D. (1965) *Nature, Lond.* **208,** 1336–1337.

MILLER, J. F. A. P. (1965) *Nature, Lond.* **208,** 1337–1338.

MUELLER, A. P., WOLFE, H. R. and MEYER, R. K. (1960) *J. Immun.* **85,** 172–179.

PIERPAOLI, W., BARONI, C., FABRIS, N. and SORKIN, E. (1969) *Immunology* **16,** 217–230.

PIERPAOLI, W. and SORKIN, E. (1967a) *Nature, Lond.* **215,** 834–837.

PIERPAOLI, W. and SORKIN, E. (1967b) *Br. J. exp. Path.* **48,** 627–631.

PIERPAOLI, W. and SORKIN, E. (1968) *J. Immun.* **101,** 1036–1043.

PIERPAOLI, W. and SORKIN, E. (1969a) In *The Immune Response and its Suppression (Antibiotica Chemother.* **15**), pp. 122–134, ed. Sorkin, E. Basel: Karger.

PIERPAOLI, W. and SORKIN, E. (1969b) In *The Lymphatic Tissue and Germinal Centers in Immune Response (Adv. exp. Med. Biol.* **5**), pp. 397–401, ed. Fiore-Donati, L. and Hanna, M. G. New York: Plenum Press.

PURVES, H. D. and GRIESBACH, W. E. (1946) *Br. J. exp. Path.* **27,** 170–179.

SHERMAN, J. D. and DAMESHEK, W. (1964) In *The Thymus in Immunobiology*, pp. 542–548, ed. Good, R. A. and Gabrielsen, A. E. New York: Harper.

SIMONSEN, M. (1962) *Prog. Allergy* **6,** 349–466.

SIPERSTEIN, E. R., NICHOLS, G. W., GRIESBACH, W. E. and CHAIKOFF, I. L. (1954) *Anat. Rec.* **118,** 593–620.

SOLOMON, J. and GREEP, R. O. (1959) *Endocrinology* **65,** 158–164.

TAYLOR, R. B. (1965) *Nature, Lond.* **208,** 1334–1335.

WARNER, N. L. and BURNET, F. M. (1961) *Aust. J. biol. Sci.* **14,** 580–587.

WILKINSON, P. C., SINGH, H. and SORKIN, E. (1970) *Immunology* **18,** 437–441.

DISCUSSION

Mühlbock: Can you give us more details of the somatotropic hormone that you use?

Pierpaoli: We have used several preparations of somatotropic hormone of bovine origin which are commercially available. Besides these, purified bovine somatotropic hormone has been kindly supplied by the Endocrinology Section of the National

Institutes of Health, Bethesda; also Professor C. H. Li sent us a highly purified preparation of bovine somatotropic hormone. We are aware of the problem that the hormone is antigenic and for this reason we had internal controls in all experiments, to see how far antigenicity is responsible for modifications in the lymphoid tissue.

Mühlbock: Have you studied the effects of prolactin on immunological competence?

Pierpaoli: We have tested the effects of prolactin in several experimental conditions; in dwarf mice for example it induces a remarkable hyperplasia of the bone marrow. But it is not yet fully established that prolactin and STH are separate hormones, at least in man. In the mouse however they appear to be distinct polypeptide molecules. Perhaps they share several peptide sequences.

Mühlbock: There is an elegant system in the mouse to induce hyperproduction of prolactin; if one implants the hypophysis from a mouse of one inbred strain into the kidney or spleen of a female mouse of the same strain, one obtains a constant high production of prolactin. There wouldn't be any problem of antigenicity in this system.

Goldstein: Drs R. J. Duquesnoy, P. K. Kalpaktsoglou and R. A. Good (1970) have confirmed your findings in the Snell-Bagg mouse, Dr Pierpaoli, and they are also looking at another strain of pituitary-deficient mice, the Ames strain. This same laboratory has also reported (Duquesnoy, Good and Sprunt 1970) that prolonged nursing with foster mothers partially reversed the deleterious influences of pituitary deficiencies on the lymphoid tissue and also partially restored the ability to respond to antigens. Have you attempted to look at this model by nursing the Snell-Bagg mice, to see whether you can circumvent this immunological deficiency?

Pierpaoli: We have worked on these dwarf mice and we came to realize their limitations for evaluating the effect of hormones on the immune capacity, because although they have an arrested development of the immune system and although they are extremely deficient in the production of growth hormone and thyroxine, they go on producing a minimal amount of these hormones, which doesn't allow us to evaluate the effect of these hormones fully. Their deficiency is only partial.

Fabris: On the point that forced nursing can enhance the immunological capacity of dwarf mice, it is to be noted that the immune deficiency of such mice cannot be due to malnourishment, because they normally feed from the mother much more than their litter mates. On the other hand the fact that dwarf mice are indistinguishable from normal litter mates for the first two or three weeks of age, that is, before weaning, suggests that either the hypophysis is not functioning at this age or the animals can receive some hormonal factors from the mother through the milk. Forced nursing could thus not simply mean overnourishment but rather a passage of hormones from the mother to the lactating animals.

Fachet: You have demonstrated convincing effects of hormones on the thymus–lymphatic system but I am doubtful about the feedback activity of thymectomy on the endocrine organs, on the grounds of our earlier experiments (Fachet *et al.* 1965). You did not measure growth hormone levels and you were showing only the changes in the granules of the hypophyseal cells in the thymectomized animals. It would be valuable to determine the growth hormone level in the hypophysis and in the blood as well. The specificity of the effects of neonatal thymectomy on the hypophyseal cells is also a bit doubtful because these mice were not kept in germ-free conditions and therefore pathogens and other environmental factors also might have affected the endocrine organs.

On the role of thyroxine, it is well established that thyroxine causes a marked enlargement of the thymus and lymphocytosis in the blood, and it does so in spite of the fact that the corticosteroid level in the blood is nearly doubled, which is quite enough to cause involution of the thymus (Fachet *et al.* 1964). Thus thyroxine causes hypertrophy of the lymphatic system in the presence of the high corticosteroid level. But we found that at the same time the thyroxine treatment doubled the transcortin level in the blood. This might mean that the transcortin-bound form of corticosteroids is increased in the circulation by thyroxine but perhaps only the free form is effective in eliciting the involution of the thymus–lymphatic system (Fachet *et al.* 1967).

Pierpaoli: We realize that we should determine the level of growth hormone in the blood and in the pituitary glands of the neonatally thymectomized mice, but we would like to have mouse growth hormone and anti-mouse-growth hormone serum for an exact determination by radioimmunoassay. This we plan to do. I fully agree that thyroxine is involved in some way in the dynamics of cells of the lymphoid system. However, in the experiments we presented we tried to determine how far thyroxine is responsible for the effects observed in the lymphatic tissue. It appeared that the involution of the lymphoid tissues induced by interfering with thyroid function, by the use of anti-thyrotropic hormone serum or thyroidectomy, could be fully prevented by giving somatotropin. This indicates that STH is acting and not thyroxine. However it is an endocrinological belief that the synthesis or release of growth hormone in the pituitary gland depends on a functioning thyroid gland.

A. White: I infer that you think that the primary thymotropic principle, which could be somatotropin, is dependent on the thyroid for its release and secretion. Have you examined the effect on the thymus of thyroid-stimulating hormone (TSH) in a hypophysectomized animal? I believe you have reported the effects of giving TSH to mice which were wasting as a result of giving anti-growth hormone serum?

In terms of ontogenesis, would it not be surprising if most features of ontogenesis were *not* modulated by the thyroid? Finally, have you looked at the level of circulating adrenocortical steroids in the dwarf mice, and what happens in these animals if they are adrenalectomized? That is, is the dwarf mouse a dwarf because of some aspect of hyperadrenocorticoidism? I make this comment because Dougherty and his colleagues (Dougherty, Berliner and Berliner 1960) have hypothesized that one aspect of neonatal thymectomy, namely the runting or wasting, as well as the lymphoid tissue involution, may be the consequence of the absence of a major gland, the thymus, which is concerned with the inactivation of adrenal steroids.

Pierpaoli: I cannot answer your first two questions because these experiments have not been done, but we are now testing TSH in hypophysectomized rats. We have observed that lymphoid tissue cellularity and the antibody response of mice treated with anti-thyrotropic hormone serum, whose thyroid function has been blocked and which show an extreme involution of the peripheral lymphoid tissue, can be fully restored with growth hormone, and not only with thyroxine and TSH.

We have not adrenalectomized the dwarf mice or measured their blood corticosteroids.

A. White: Thymoma associated with thyrotoxicosis has been described in the clinical literature. I think this is another classical example of the proliferative effect of thyroid hormone on lymphoid tissue.

Fabris: In order to evaluate the importance of a relatively high level of corticosteroids in the immunological deficiency of dwarf mice we have looked at the adrenals of these animals by histochemical methods. The adrenals are hypotrophic and synthesis of corticosteroids seemed reduced, probably as a consequence of a hypophyseal defect in ACTH production. However, it should be pointed out that Snell-Bagg dwarfism is a recessive character produced on a heterogeneous background. Therefore, besides the main hypophyseal hormone deficiency in STH in dwarf mice, slightly different breeding conditions can be responsible for a certain variability in other pituitary hormonal deficiencies.

Goldstein: We have recently confirmed the early work of Cohen and co-workers (1963) that thymocytes of newborn mice are immunologically competent to elicit a graft-versus-host response. I was surprised to see that newborn thymocytes in your system were not competent. If you used larger numbers of newborn thymocytes, you might see a response.

Pierpaoli: In our strain combination fortunately the thymocytes of newborns seem to be incompetent to elicit a GVH response, but perhaps we shouldn't say that we *induce* their competence; we probably increase with STH the number of competent cells in the thymocyte preparation. The hormone may not switch on immune differentiation but may amplify it in a *determining* manner.

Goldstein: What is interesting is that when the number of thymocytes are too few to elicit a normal GVH response, the thymotropic principle can lower the threshold for immune responsiveness.

Pierpaoli: Yes. I am anxious to see whether the modifications induced in the pituitary by removing the neonatal thymus can be reversed by thymus factors. This would be a classical endocrinological experiment, if the effect of thymectomy could be reversed by an extract of the missing gland. It could show that growth hormone directly or through other hormones controls cells in the epithelial or lymphoid part of the thymus which secrete the thymus factor. My only doubt is about the specificity of this factor—whether it is a distinct molecular entity.

R. G. White: How long a contact do you think is required with STH to make the thymocytes effective?

Pierpaoli: To answer this, one should do a series of experiments using different doses of the hormone and evaluating the spleen indices each day for an eight-day period. We have calculated the spleen index usually 8 days after injection of the cells and daily injections of 100 μg STH. This dose has been suggested by Professor Li; it probably seems very high to endocrinologists!

R. G. White: Presumably you could also try to curtail the effect of STH by using antiserum to STH, in order to define a minimum period of contact.

Pierpaoli: It seems that newborn rodents produce very little, if any, STH. The action of anti-STH serum in adult, and, in this specific case in newborn, mice is not easy to interpret and the dose would be problematic; it would presumably be a neutralization of the injected STH with anti-STH antibody. Our experiments using the GVH assay are based on the assumption that the mice are immunologically deficient because they lack certain hormones, being endocrinologically immature; we can presumably speed the differentiation of the competent cells by supplying what they lack for a further step of their differentiation. This would show that immunological and endocrinological maturation proceed in parallel and are interdependent.

R. G. White: You don't need an intact thymus for the effect, because you can show it in a thymectomized mouse; this leaves open the possibility of a direct effect of STH on the thymocytes.

Pierpaoli: We have done the same type of experiment using thymocytes from embryo mice killed at between 12 and 15 days of pregnancy and injecting a large number of these thymocytes into normal or neonatally thymectomized F_1 hybrid recipients. We were unable to see any effect of the embryonic cells in inducing a GVH reaction, or any enhancement by growth hormone of the immunocompetence of these cells. There seem therefore to be very specific stages of differentiation of the lymphoid system which are *not* dependent on growth hormone.

Owen: There is accruing evidence in the mouse that the cells which one injects in a thymocyte suspension which induce a graft-versus-host reaction are not typical of the majority of cells in the thymus but are a minor population, for example those thymus cells which have lost TL antigen (Leckband 1970). This suggests that in your graft-versus-host system, STH is acting on this type of cell. There is also the possibility that the hormone may be acting on host spleen cells as well since, in most mouse strains, splenomegaly is host in origin.

Lance: Dr Pierpaoli, are the newborn recipients in your graft-versus-host system deficient in STH?

Pierpaoli: Yes. We think that the injected STH is acting on the cells we inject into the newborn recipients, because the recipients secrete no, or very little STH themselves, and the injected cells derive from newborn donors.

Sorkin: Dr Lance's question is quite justified and the answer is that we don't know the actual level of STH in the newborn recipients, but we assume that it is very low.

Pierpaoli: There is information on the amount of growth hormone in the pituitary glands of newborn and adult rodents. There are light microscopy studies (Siperstein *et al.* 1954), and radioimmunoassays have been done (Daughaday *et al.* 1968). It seems that a significant amount of growth hormone does not begin to be secreted in the pituitary gland of rodents until several days after birth, and in fact the development of the embryo and growth in the early stages of life in some species seems to be independent of growth hormone (Hoet 1969). This is shown by decapitating the foetus *in utero*; the foetus grows almost normally until birth (Jost 1961). Newborn animals may receive growth factors from the mother during lactation. Our graft-versus-host response model is based on the possibility of forcing a physiological process to occur by anticipating what will happen later, that is by giving hormones before the animal itself secretes enough of them. This opens up the possibility that induction of tolerance in newborn mice is dependent not only on their immunological but also on their endocrinological immaturity at birth. Therefore an experimental approach exists to study the induction of tolerance in the neonatal period and to see how far hormones can interfere with or speed these processes of immunological differentiation.

Szenberg: You showed micrographs of the pituitary where you had some kind of feedback mechanism in the young thymectomized animals on the cells producing growth hormone. What happens if you take out the thymus in an adult animal, which is immunologically competent? Does removal of the thymus cause changes in the cells producing growth hormone?

Pierpaoli: We have some indication from light microscopy only. I was unable to see any change in the growth hormone-producing cells (acidophilic cells) in the pituitary after adult thymectomy. But this type of experiment must be extended, and we expect that by refining the techniques and by using electron microscopy we should see changes in the pituitary after adult thymectomy, perhaps when combined with X-irradiation.

Szenberg: But this is the problem. If you thymectomize an adult you just remove an organ; you don't influence the immune competence of the animal, as you do when you thymectomize the newborn. So the problem is, are the cells producing growth hormone being influenced by removal of the thymus as such, or are they being influenced by the consequences of the removal, namely the immunological trouble in which the animal now finds itself? This is a very important question, because in one case you would have direct feedback by some product of the thymus on the production of growth hormone, and I don't think this is the case. In the other situation you have just a general immunological malaise, which might influence all kinds of things, including production of growth hormone. It would be important to decide between these two effects.

Ernström: Dr Pierpaoli, you have demonstrated the importance of growth hormone in the development of cell-mediated immunity. Do the growth hormone and thyroxine have a similar effect on humoral immunity?

Pierpaoli: In the system with neonatally thymectomized mice the deficient or absent capacity of these animals to produce antibody against sheep erythrocytes is not affected by giving growth hormone. However we do not have conclusive data, especially as far as cellular immunity is concerned.

Sorkin: One can suppress antibody production by giving anti-STH serum. If one injects normal rabbit gamma globulin into mice and compares its effect with anti-STH rabbit gamma globulin it becomes evident that anti-STH globulin suppresses antibody production to itself. Thus STH action is somehow connected with antibody production. How and in what way, we do not know. STH is known to affect ribosome synthesis (Tata 1966) and messenger RNA synthesis (Korner 1964) so that it might act on antibody production in this way; or it may also have effects on cell membranes, once antigen has interacted with specific receptors.

Ernström: Cells exported from the thymus might be important for the humoral immune response, interacting perhaps with bone marrow cells. If this export of thymic cells is regulated and increased by these hormones, directly or indirectly, growth hormone and thyroxine should stimulate the humoral immune response.

Pierpaoli: Immunological maturity of our strain of Charles River mice is partially developed at birth because even if they are neonatally thymectomized, they still are able to produce antibody against some antigens, while cellular immunity is impaired. Therefore some specific steps of immune differentiation in mice apparently take place before birth. This doesn't allow us to say whether growth hormone is required for the formation or differentiation of antibody-producing cells; perhaps we could determine this with another system. Our data seem to indicate that two or more different cell compartments are in time and sequentially sensitive to the effect of growth hormone or other hormones. It may be that growth hormone is no longer required in the neonatal period for the formation of antibody-producing cells, while other compartments are still hormone-dependent.

Fabris: Dr Pierpaoli and Dr Sorkin (1969) have shown that one can impair humoral immune responses with anti-STH antiserum in 3–4-week-old mice. On the other hand, dwarf mice show a slight delay in the humoral immune responses to sheep red cells or bovine serum albumin (unpublished results). These findings speak in favour of an effect of STH on humoral immune responses. Because neither treatment with STH in normal animals, nor removal of the hypophysis in the adult, are able to modify the humoral immune response, other systems with normal adult animals were used, in which immune responses were depressed by cortisol (Fabris, Pierpaoli and Sorkin 1970) or by sub-lethal X-irradiation, as reported by Duquesnoy and co-workers (1969). STH could in fact reverse the depressed immune response, but it still leaves open the question of whether STH is needed for an immune response in adult life. As one working hypothesis, one can presume that during ontogenetic development a pool of lymphocytes is created under the influence of STH and other hormones. Although these cells may still be hormone-sensitive when called on to mount an immune response, we are perhaps unable to demonstrate a later STH action of this kind with our present techniques.

Fachet: Do you think STH is having a specific effect on the maturation of the immune system? This hormone has many effects on other organs and tissues, influencing their metabolism. These effects should be considered in interpreting the effectiveness of the STH treatment, especially in developing animals. We perhaps shouldn't consider growth hormone only as a specific thymotropic hormone, therefore.

Pierpaoli: I agree; STH has many effects at many levels. STH may be really only required critically during ontogenesis or in adult life for a particular step in the differentiation of certain cell types. Considering what a complex polypeptide molecule it is, one should perhaps not expect it to have one effect only. This molecule may have acquired new capacities and potentialities during evolution. After all, another complex polypeptide hormone, prolactin, occurs in lower vertebrates as well as in higher mammals and has apparently acquired new functions in evolution.

REFERENCES

COHEN, M. W., THORBECKE, G. J., HOCHWALD, G. M. and JACOBSON, E. B. (1963) *Proc. Soc. exp. Biol. Med.* **114,** 242.

DAUGHADAY, W. H., PEAKE, G. T., BIRGE, C. A. and MARIZ, K. (1968) In *Growth Hormone*, pp. 238–252, ed. Pecile, A. and Müller, E. E. Amsterdam: Excerpta Medica Foundation. (International Congress Series No. 158.)

DOUGHERTY, T. F., BERLINER, M. L. and BERLINER, D. L. (1960) *Endocrinology* **66,** 550.

DUQUESNOY, R. J., GOOD, R. A. and SPRUNT, O. H. (1970) *Fedn Proc. Fedn Am. Socs exp. Biol.* **29**(2), 825 (abst. 3276).

DUQUESNOY, R. J., KALPAKTSOGLOU, P. K. and GOOD, R. A. (1970) *Proc. Soc. exp. Biol. Med.* **133,** 201.

DUQUESNOY, R. J., RODEY, G. E., HOLMES, B. and GOOD, R. A. (1969) *Fedn Proc. Fedn Am. Socs exp. Biol.* **28**(2), 376 (abst. 664).

FABRIS, N., PIERPAOLI, W. and SORKIN, E. (1970) In *Developmental Aspects of Antibody Formation and Structure*. Prague: Publishing House of the Czechoslovak Academy of Science. In press.

FACHET, J., McINTOSH, B., LABRIE, F. and FORTIER, C. (1967) *Acta physiol. hung.* **32,** 43.

FACHET, J., STARK, E., PALKOVITS, M. and MIHALY, K. (1965) *Acta med. hung.* **21,** 297.

FACHET, J., VALLENT, K., PALKOVITS, M. and ACR, S. (1964) *Acta med. hung.* **20,** 281.

HOET, J. J. (1969) *Ciba Fdn Symp. Foetal Autonomy,* pp. 186–217. London: Churchill.

JOST, A. (1961) *Harvey Lect.* **55,** 201–226.

KORNER, A. (1964) *Biochem. J.* **92,** 449.

LECKBAND, E. (1970) *Fedn Proc. Fedn Am. Socs exp. Biol.* **29**(2), 621 (abst. 2108).

PIERPAOLI, W. and SORKIN, E. (1969) In *The Immune Response and its Suppression (Antibiotica Chemother.* **15**), pp. 122–134, ed. Sorkin, E. Basel: Karger.

SIPERSTEIN, E., NICHOLS, C. W. Jr, GRIESBACH, W. E. and CHAIKOFF, I. L. (1954) *Anat. Rec.* **118,** 593–608.

TATA, J. R. (1966) In *Developmental and Metabolic Control Mechanisms and Neoplasia,* pp. 335–356. Anderson Hospital and Tumor Institute. Baltimore: Williams and Wilkins.

GENERAL DISCUSSION

Goldstein: To open the discussion, we would like to present, for your critical comments, our present working hypothesis on the mechanism of action of thymosin. It may be possible to fit much of what has been presented here into a general scheme. In addition, I might comment on the important role of the pituitary in the expression of thymic function.

As described in our paper, we have suggested a division of the thymus-dependent, immunologically competent cells into two broad, probably heterogeneous, classes, *A* and *B* (see Fig. 3, p. 15). In addition we suggest a third class of cells, *C*, which we call potential antibody-producing cells. The latter class includes the cells that have been found to act synergistically with an immunologically competent cell in the humoral antibody response (Clamen, Chaperon and Triplett 1966). We believe, from our recent studies as well as from evidence in the literature, that at least two types of development of immunologically competent lymphocytes are possible in the mouse system: a peripheral development, occurring outside the thymus, and a central development that has to occur within the thymus. It appears that peripheral development is influenced significantly by thymosin and possibly other thymic humoral factors which act upon stem cell populations at sites removed from the thymus. These stem cells may include cells that early in their development have been in the thymus or have come under its influence, such as the post-thymic cells described by Drs Stutman, Yunis and Good (1969). By "stem cell" we mean the cell from which may develop the cells involved in immunological reactions. Under the influence of thymosin these stem cells can be activated to react immunologically. We use the term "activated" because we are not yet certain whether it is an immediate derepression mechanism or a more prolonged maturation process. The suggestion that maturation of Class *A* cells occurs rapidly and may involve a derepression mechanism derives from evidence from several lines of recent investigations in our laboratory.

(1) Stem cell populations incubated with thymosin *in vitro* for

a brief period (1½ hours) contain a population of cells capable of participating in a graft-versus-host (GVH) response *in vivo* (see our paper, p. 10).

(2) Embryonic thymocytes shortly before birth are unable to elicit a GVH response *in vivo*, but immediately after birth (6 hours) now contain a population of cells capable of inducing a typical GVH response (A. L. Goldstein, A. Guha and A. White, in preparation).

(3) Embryonic thymocytes are unable to recognize transplantation or differentiation antigens when incubated *in vitro* with allogeneic or isogeneic spleen cells, but shortly after birth can do so (Howe, Goldstein and Battisto 1970).

The above findings, together with those described in our studies with bone marrow cells in the paper reported here (p. 10), point to the existence of a population of stem cells within which resides a population of latent cells which can be stimulated by thymosin to accelerate the maturation of their immunological competence. A process appears to occur within a relatively short period of time which resembles a derepression; this is a possible locus of action of the pituitary, initiating the production and secretion of thymosin by the epithelial cells at about the time of birth. This process apparently results in the production of large numbers of Class *A* cells shortly after birth. The fact that neonatal thymectomy severely cripples cell-mediated immunity (Class *A* mediated) strengthens the argument that most of the cells involved in cell-mediated immunological phenomena exhibit competence only shortly after birth.

I don't believe that the thymus environment *per se* is essential for the development of Class *A* cells. These can develop in or out of the thymus, but the main factor distinguishing these cells is that they only require the endocrine influence of the thymus. We have most recently explored, in collaboration with Drs Howe and Battisto (Howe, Goldstein and Battisto 1970) another assay system which is believed to reflect in part an *in vitro* cell-mediated response, namely the mixed lymphocyte interaction. We have looked at the capacity of thymic cells from embryonic and new-born mice to recognize transplantation antigens and differentiation antigens on the surface of spleen cells from a number of isogeneic and allogeneic mouse strains. In the first system we have examined the capacity of thymocytes from CBA mice to recognize F_1 spleen cells (CBA × C57Bl/6) from adult (60–day–old) mice during a 5-day incubation period *in vitro* using [^{14}C]thymidine incorporation as an index of cell stimulation. We have found that thymocytes from 19-day-old CBA embryos, which are totally unreactive in this assay, acquire shortly after birth the capacity to recognize the F_1 cells as foreign and respond to them, as reflected in blast cell formation. This capacity of the thymocyte is maximal between 2 and 3 days after birth and then declines gradually with age, so that by age 60 days the response is minimal. By prior incubation of each cell population with mitomycin C, which prevents DNA synthesis (Bach and Voynow 1966), we have established that at least 90 per cent of the mixed lymphocyte reaction is due to the recognition of the F_1 cells by the thymocytes through a process that is apparently initiated abruptly at birth.

In additional studies Dr Howe, Dr Battisto and I have looked at a totally isogeneic system by incubating thymocytes from newborn CBA/J mice with 60-day-old spleen cells from CBA/J mice in a mixed culture *in vitro* (CBA/J→CBA/J). The data reveal that a thymocyte can recognize self; that is, it can recognize the "foreignness" of spleen cells from genetically identical mice; there is recognition of spleen-specific differentiation antigens. The results indicate that this type of recognition also begins shortly after birth, reaches a maximum 2 to 3 days postnatally and falls, more rapidly than the F_1 system, to control levels at about 60 days. It has also been established, by prior incubation of each population of cells separately with mitomycin C, that the response ([^{14}C]thymidine incorporation) resides primarily in the thymocyte. These recent findings provide strong evidence for rapid maturation processes occurring at birth or shortly after birth which enable the thymocytes to become immunologically competent cells.

The second large class of thymus-dependent cells (Class *B*), which we designate thymus "activated" cells, migrate into the thymus, where, in addition to a possible requirement of a humoral influence, the thymus environment is needed for development and/or expansion of cell populations which are immunologically competent. The development of Class *B* cells might also involve a relatively short activating process. This is the cell type which is involved in a cooperative manner with non-thymus-dependent cell populations in antibody production. The direct evidence to support the concept that a thymic locus is necessary for the maturation of Class B cells derives from experiments in the neonatally thymectomized or adult-thymectomized lethally irradiated, bone-marrow-treated mouse (Goldstein *et al*. 1970). We have found that thymosin can reconstitute cell-mediated capacities in the absence of an intact thymus, but does not restore the capacity to make 19S or 7S antibody to sheep erythrocytes.

Humphrey: Your thesis is that something happens at birth which turns on the thymus cells so that they become immuno-competent. Are you implying that these are not cells migrating in from elsewhere, but cells which were in the thymus the day before birth and are in the thymus the day after birth, and something happens to those cells?

Goldstein: They may be both cells indigenous to the thymus and cells that have migrated into the thymus. What we are suggesting is that the endowment of competence to Class A cells in the thymus may be dependent upon the increased humoral secretions induced by some mechanism triggered by the process of birth.

Owen: I agree that an important developmental event may take place in the thymus around the time of birth but this is the end point of other important changes beginning well before birth. Thus by removing the embryonic thymus and testing its capacity to become lymphoid *in vitro*, we have shown that stem cells first enter the thymic anlage at about 11 days' gestation. During the course of the next 6 to 7 days there is an intense proliferation of cells within the thymus and the organ becomes organized into medulla and cortex packed with lymphocytes. The alloantigens θ and TL are not expressed on the surface of cells within the thymus before 14 days' gestation. However, M. C. Raff and I have shown that if the thymus is removed at this stage and cultured *in vitro* for 4 days, the lymphoid cells then present are strongly positive for θ and TL. Thus a maturation stage occurs before birth and is accompanied by the expression of alloantigens on the cell surface. The further differentiation of these cells into immunologically competent cells may involve the loss of TL and a reduction in θ (Boyse and Old 1969). This second step probably does occur at about the time of birth, and possibly first within the thymus.

Goldstein: I agree that there are many complex events which occur in and on the lymphocyte before and after birth. The formation and loss of TL antigens is a case in point. This antigen is found only on thymocytes while they reside in the thymus and is only seen in cells in the peripheral circulation in leukaemic animals. It has been suggested that the TL-positive cells are the precursors of mature immunologically competent cells (Leckband 1970). This hypothesis has been strengthened by Dr Leckband's observation that the cells in the thymus of newborn TL-positive congeneic C57Bl/6 mice that are competent to induce a graft-versus-host response reside in a small population (< 10 per cent of total thymic cells) and are all TL-negative. It remains to be established whether the TL-negative cells contain a population of cells which can also cooperate with Class C cells to elicit humoral immune responses.

It may be noted that although Class A cells are lacking in the population of cells in the 19-day-old embryonic thymus, Class B cells are present in numbers large enough to elicit cooperative effects and a positive response to sheep erythrocyte antigens (MacGillivray, Mayhew and Rose 1970). This suggests that Class B cells develop earlier than Class A cells and during the late stages of foetal development (18–21 days) apparently migrate into the thymus where they undergo final maturation and/or expansion. The fact that one of the few antigenic responses influenced by neonatal thymectomy in mice is that exemplified by the response to the sheep erythrocyte antigen suggests a possible sequential maturation of this class of B cells which is not quite completed at birth. A sequential maturation in the thymus before birth would explain why, when the thymus is removed at birth, the cells which recognize this particular type of antigen are still in the thymus, whereas other classes of B cells, which recognize other types of antigens, have perhaps gone into the thymus, have developed and expanded, and have departed from the thymus before birth, and hence are not influenced by neonatal thymectomy since they are already in the peripheral circulation. In fact it has not been shown conclusively that it is necessary for all Class B cells to enter the thymus in order to acquire the capacity to recognize such antigens as sheep erythrocytes. For example, there is evidence that stem cells that have never been in the thymus can recognize sheep red cell antigens (Tyan, Herzenberg and Gibbs 1969). Thus, the thymic locus may be necessary for the expansion of a given population of cells and the high mitotic index characteristic of the thymus is a reflection of the production of large numbers of Class *B* cells.

The observation that the level of thoracic duct lymphocytes cannot be restored to normal with thymosin treatment either in the neonatally thymectomized animal or in the adult-thymecto-mized animal indicates that a large number of these circulating cells are probably Class *B* cells and, in terms of overall numbers, there may be more Class *B* cells in the thoracic duct circulation than Class *A* cells. The question of cell types and possible categories of the thymus-dependent class in the thoracic lymphatic circulation is not at the moment clearly defined.

Humphrey: Are you saying that the cells which *don't* go through the thymus can, with the help of thymosin, elicit cell-mediated immunity?

Goldstein: I am saying that in order to elicit cell-mediated reactions a thymic *locus* is not required since the thymic humoral factor will promote maturation peripherally. We are only beginning to understand the importance of specific lymphoid loci for the proper development of classes of lymphocyte. Dr J. R. Battisto, Dr L. C. Cantor, Dr J. F. Borek, Miss E. Cabrerra and I have reported (1969) that the genetically spleenless mouse is unable to produce certain specific types of antibodies. For example, this mouse will make $7S\gamma_1$ antibody but not the hetero-cytotrophic $7S\gamma_2$ antibody. This indicates that, at least for the maturation of certain classes of cells, a spleen locus is critical at some point in development. A similar situation may be true with the thymus; the latter may be involved in expanding a population of cells which can already recognize antigens, and this may be the explanation of the high mitotic rate in the thymus, rather than solely a reflection of the elimination of forbidden clones.

Humphrey: At some stage diversity of antigenic response has to be generated; the evidence suggests that the total diversity of responses which an animal is capable of making increases during embryonic development. The hard evidence isn't very great, and is largely confined to the sheep, and the rest is really inferential (see, for example, Sterzl and Silverstein 1967). But one of the unproved hypotheses is that diversity is generated during repeated cell divisions. The thymus is one site where a great deal of mitosis of lymphocytes takes place; the bone marrow is a second, and germinal centres are a third. In what other part of the body is this so?

Owen: The main sites of haemopoietic stem cell renewal in the embryo are the yolk sac, and in the mammal the foetal liver also (Moore and Metcalf 1970).

Humphrey: So it's an interesting question to what extent foetal liver cells are immunologically competent, or would be made immunologically competent with the help of thymosin.

Owen: That's a crucial experiment.

Szenberg: A problem with your hypothesis, Dr Goldstein, is that only a small proportion of the cells in the thymus are at any time immunologically competent cells, perhaps 5 per cent, and of these 5 per cent, only 2 per cent, according to what we know in mice and chickens, can react to any given histocompatibility antigen. So there is a relatively high proportion of cells able to recognize a given histocompatibility antigen, whereas only one in one or two million cells is able to recognize an antigenic determinant like the one you used for induction of antibody, namely sheep red cells. So a thymus may contain 200 or 300 cells which are able to produce a graft-versus-host reaction, and no cells, or maybe one cell, which is able to recognize any other type of antigen. So it is not surprising that you are able to "induce" graft-versus-host activity by using something which may increase the mitotic activity of the cells, such as thymosin, whereas because you haven't any cells able to recognize other antigenic determinants—it does not affect the argument whether it is antibody or cell-mediated immunity—you have nothing to multiply. This quantitative factor may be important in drawing conclusions from this type of experiment.

Secondly, I don't know why you need to invoke derepression; you can mature the lymphoid system earlier, in the embryo, if you bring antigen into the system. This has been shown by several investigators (La Via, Rowlands and Block 1963; Silverstein *et al.* 1963; Silverstein 1962; Schinkel and Ferguson 1953). So birth is not something critical. In some strains of mice immunological maturation is earlier than birth and neonatal thymectomy does not cause runting. In rabbits, neonatal thymectomy does not affect the development of cell-mediated immunity. Guinea pigs mature immunologically before birth.

In a normal animal the thymus population of small lymphocytes is replenished every three days; the release of immunocompetent cells from the thymus may start before the birth of the animal or after birth, depending on the species and strain. I do not think you can postulate dramatic events taking place in the immunological system at birth.

Goldstein: I don't disagree with you; we are discussing different types of systems. I didn't mean to imply that a large number of cells within the thymus can elicit a GVH response. It is generally recognized that you need approximately 10 times the number of thymocytes to elicit a GVH response, in comparison to other lymphoid cell populations. The point is that however small this population is, you can detect it in sufficiently sensitive systems. I agree that the GVH system is a difficult one to use since one does not know how much of the response is host and how much is donor contribution and how much is due to inflammation. The mixed lymphocyte interaction however is a very sensitive system; one can work with small, known numbers of cells and there is no problem of cells coming into or leaving the system. In the mixed lymphocyte reaction it is clear that whatever the process is that enables thymocytes to recognize foreign antigens, it is a relatively rapid phenomenon. Antibody-producing capacity is certainly developed before birth: as you say, Silverstein and co-workers (1963) showed that the foetal lamb, for example, can respond to many antigens. The main point I wanted to make is that the development of cell-mediated thymic competence at birth could be a derepression phenomenon, because we know that hormones can exert rapid effects *in vitro*.

Korner: Can you inject hormones into the 19-day-old embryo and get a response from its thymocytes in your GVH or mixed lymphocyte systems?

Goldstein: We have not yet attempted this.

Pierpaoli: Hormones might have the capacity to determine the differentiation of cells, changing their antigenic determinants, or provoking the formation of new antigenic determinants. Indirect evidence for this comes from Triplett's experiments (1962). He removed the pituitary gland from embryos of the tree frog, *Hila regilla*, before the metamorphic stage and then the explanted organs were returned to the original donors, *after* the frog had reached the metamorphic stage 60 days later. The animals rejected their own tissue which had not undergone the same differentiation as the donors, which were fed with beef thyroid powder in order that metamorphosis should take place without the pituitary. The point I want to stress is that Triplett did not consider at all the possible role played by the hormone in the differentiation process.

Humphrey: His hypothesis was that the animal had ceased to be tolerant of its own tissues, which is a different principle altogether.

Gunn: If you take a skin graft from one rat and put it temporarily on another rat of a different strain and then after 24 or 48 hours transfer it back to the original donor the majority of grafts will be rejected, whereas they will be accepted if the transfer is made in a syngeneic system (Brautbar, Nelken and Boss 1969). Therefore it may be wrong to read too much into the Triplett type of experiment.

King: There are examples of hormones changing the genetic competence of cells. For example with either mammary gland in organ culture (Voytovich, Owens and Topper 1969) or chick oviduct *in vivo* (O'Malley *et al.* 1969), one hormone induces cell division and the new cells can then respond either to different hormones (mammary gland) or differently to the same hormone (oviduct). So there are precedents for Dr Goldstein's idea.

Humphrey: The idea that there might be a specific maturation factor(s) for immunologically competent cells is attractive. It could provide an explanation for the observation that persons who are severely hypogammaglobulinaemic, with normal cell-mediated immunity and presumably with a functioning thymus, but who are able to make only minimal amounts of immunoglobulins, and have to be kept going for several years by regular passive transfer of human immunoglobulin, sometimes begin to make immunoglobulin at normal rates and at least to make enough antibodies to maintain normal health. Such people have not been given a new set of stem cells, but something has happened to enable their own immunologically competent cells, whatever their derivation, to secrete antibody. I remember the late J. R. Squire, chairman of the Medical Research Council's Working Party on Hypogammaglobulinaemia, insisting that there must be some missing maturation factor. Nobody has succeeded in isolating such a maturation factor, and there are of course other possible explanations. Nevertheless one might also argue that adjuvants could act by producing local maturation factors, in addition to any function in maintaining a depot of antigen. The most effective adjuvants cause very marked local activation of macrophages, and it is in the immediate neighbourhood of these that lymphocytes are stimulated to differentiate and to proliferate. By no means all of the immunoglobulin which they produce is identifiable as specific antibody (Humphrey 1963). Furthermore there is some suggestive evidence that activated macrophages can stimulate lymphocytes non-specifically (Unanue, Askonas and Allison 1969). It might be interesting to look for a maturation factor in adjuvant granulomata, for example, along similar lines to the search for thymus factors.

These approaches are complementary rather than contradictory to that of Dr Pierpaoli, Dr Sorkin and Dr Fabris. They are studying hormones which can affect many kinds of cell but are particularly important for certain cells at certain stages of development. We know very little about whether their effects on lymphocytes are direct or secondary to differentiation of other cells such as neighbouring epithelium. Although I suspect that it will be necessary to improve the assay systems before probing very much deeper, I am sure that the right sort of questions are being asked.

It would be useful to apply to experimentally altered lymphocytes the kind of tests which Dr Lance described, since these give valuable information additional to knowing whether or not the lymphocytes can induce a graft-versus-host or a mixed lymphocyte reaction. Knowledge of the migration patterns provided certainly helped to clarify the mode of action of ALS and the synergistic effect of cortisol. I now see the rationale for a remark made by Sir Michael Woodruff at a recent meeting of the Medical Research Council's Working Party on ALS to the effect that he would never consider administering ALS without also giving small amounts of cortisol as a precaution against sensitization. Evidently the combination is likely to have important practical value for other reasons as well.

Dr Ambrose's thesis about the need for physiological levels of cortisol for the proper development of immunological responsiveness, like many truths, seems almost obvious once it has been stated; he deserves our congratulations for analysing a difficult *in vitro* system and showing that the effect of serum, which nearly everyone uses, is entirely replaceable by cortisol and that its concentration must be close to that occurring normally in the circulation. Furthermore, he has gone some way to indicating how cortisol acts at the biochemical level. I hope that his work has brought the subject nearer to the realm of interest of Professor Korner and Dr King, namely how the hormone receptors interact, what they are, what mechanisms are derepressed, and so on. In the light of Dr Ambrose's findings a derepression mechanism seems to be a very reasonable thing to look for.

We could probably continue speculating for another day without penetrating much further into the field which Drs Pierpaoli, Sorkin and Fabris have begun to open up. They have served notice of its importance, and have mentioned many experiments which they propose to do. We must await the answers to these, and hope that they will combine them with analyses by other approaches, such as study of the capacity of cells from deprived mice to elicit graft-versus-host responses.

This has been a stimulating and worthwhile discussion, and I am sure that if Peter Medawar had been listening he would not have been disappointed. I would like to thank both the speakers and the discussants for taking part, and to express our deep gratitude to the Ciba Foundation—Dr Wolstenholme and his staff—who organize these meetings so well.

REFERENCES

BACH, F. H. and VOYNOW, H. K. (1966) *Science* **153**, 545.

BATTISTO, J. R., CANTOR, L. C., BOREK, J. F., GOLDSTEIN, A. L. and CABRERRA, E. (1969) *Nature, Lond.* **222**, 1196.

BOYSE, E. A. and OLD, L. J. (1969) *A. Rev. Genet.* **3**, 269.

BRAUTBAR, C., NELKEN, D. and BOSS, J. H. (1969) *Transplantation* **8**, 121.

CLAMEN, H. N., CHAPERON, E. A. and TRIPLETT, R. F. (1966) *Proc. Soc. exp. Biol. Med.* **122**, 1167.

GOLDSTEIN, A. L., ASANUMA, Y., BATTISTO, J. R., HARDY, M. A., QUINT, J. and WHITE, A. (1970) *J. Immun.* **104**, 359.

HOWE, M., GOLDSTEIN, A. L. and BATTISTO, J. R. (1970) *Proc. V Leukocyte Culture Conference*, in press.

HUMPHREY, J. H. (1963) In *La Tolérance acquise et la tolérance naturelle à l'égard de substances antigéniques définies*, p. 401. Paris: Centre National de la Recherche Scientifique.

LA VIA, M. F., ROWLANDS, D. T. Jr and BLOCK, M. (1963) *Science* **140**, 1219–1220.

LECKBAND, E. (1970) *Fedn Proc. Fedn Am. Socs exp. Biol.* **29**(2), 621 (abst. 2108).

MACGILLIVRAY, M. H., MAYHEW, B. and ROSE, N. B. (1970) *Proc. Soc. exp. Biol. Med.* **133**, 688.

MOORE, M. A. S. and METCALF, D. (1970) *Br. J. Haemat.* **18**, 279.

O'MALLEY, B. W., McGUIRE, W. L., KOHLER, P. O. and KORENMAN, S. G. (1969) *Recent Prog. Horm. Res.* **25**, 105–153.

SCHINKEL, P. G. and FERGUSON, K. A. (1953) *Aust. J. Biol. Sci.* **6**, 533.

SILVERSTEIN, A. M. (1962) *Nature, Lond.* **194**, 196–197.

SILVERSTEIN, A. M., UHR, J. W., KRANER, K. L. and LUKES, R. J. (1963) *J. exp. Med.* **117**, 799–812.

STERZL, J. and SILVERSTEIN, A. M. (1967) *Adv. Immun.* **6**, 337.

STUTMAN, O., YUNIS, E. J. and GOOD, R. A. (1969) *Transplantn. Proc.* **1**, 614.

TRIPLETT, E. L. (1962) *J. Immun.* **89**, 505–510.

TYAN, M. L., HERZENBERG, L. A. and GIBBS, P. R. (1969) *J. Immun.* **103**, 1283.

UNANUE, E. R., ASKONAS, B. A. and ALLISON, A. C. (1969) *J. Immun.* **103**, 71.

VOYTOVICH, A. E., OWENS, I. S. and TOPPER, Y. J. (1969) *Proc. natn. Acad. Sci. U.S.A.* **63**, 213–217.

SUBJECT INDEX*

* Subject Index prepared by Mr. William Hill.

Thyroxine,
  effect on chicken thymus, 44, 48
  effect on humoral immunity, 150
  effect on immunocompetence, 131, 135
  effect on runt disease, 131
  effect on thymus, 44, 48, 145
  interrelation with insulin and growth hormone, 136–138

Tumour growth, resistance to, effect of thymosin, 11–13

Wasting disease, 3, 47
  development, 139
  effect of hormones, 130
  effect of spleen cells and growth hormone, 131
  sex differences, 49